ATTENDING YOUR GRANDCHILD'S BIRTH

ATTENDING YOUR GRANDCHILD'S BIRTH

A Guide For Grandparents

By

Carolynn Bauer Zorn

What to expect and what you can do during the delivery of your grandchild.

ISBN 1-58500-799-4

**Publisher's Cataloging-in-Publication
(Provided by Quality Books, Inc.)**

Zorn, Carolynn Bauer.
Attending your grandchild's birth : a guide for
    grandparents: what to expect and what you can
    do during the delivery of your grandchild / by
    Carolynn Bauer Zorn. –1st ed.
        p. cm.
        Includes index.
        LCCN: 99-96821
        ISBN: 1-58500-799-4

        1. Childbirth—Miscellanea. 2. Grandparents.
    I. Title

RG525.Z67 1999   618.4
                             QBI99-1441

1st Books-rev. 8/29/00

This book is meant to share information but should not be used in place of appropriate medical direction. The author has used respected sources many of which are listed in the resource section. But with ongoing research, changes in pregnancy management, and infant and child care practices, it is possible that some of the information may be invalidated. Due to the personal nature of the subject, the author's feelings about many things color much of her text. She makes no apologies for this.

About the Book

Have you been invited to attend the birth of your grandchild? Are you reluctant to go or are you looking forward to it?

In her book, *Attending Your Grandchild's Birth: A Guide for Grandparents*, Carolynn Bauer Zorn, a grandmother who has been there, answers your questions about what happens during a routine hospital birth and what you can do if you are there.

If it has been twenty years since you were in a maternity ward, you probably realize that things have changed a lot. Perhaps you were sedated during the birth of your children and have never actually seen a baby being born. This book will prepare you for the birth experience by providing basic information, useful tips, little known or obscure facts and personal birth stories. By witnessing the birth of your grandchild, you will be sharing a moment in history that is life changing - a life transition for all - as you become a grandparent and your children become parents.

Besides birth techniques and labor management practices, *Attending Your Grandchild's Birth* also has a chapter on ways a parent can be responsive and helpful to a daughter or daughter-in-law during her pregnancy and a chapter which covers safety information for a grandchild's visit. This book is required reading for all the millions of baby-boomers who are becoming grandparents whether they decide to attend the actual birth or not.

Advance Praise for Attending Your Grandchild's Birth

".. the book is great. You've found a niche and filled it well. I really like the sections on acupressure and relaxation techniques, as well as (your comments about) being helpful and deferring to the father in most situations -- really important. I think that everyone present in a delivery should educate themselves."

Susan Taylor, M. D.
UCLA Hospital
Santa Monica, CA

"In Attending Your Grandchild's Birth" author Carolynn Bauer Zorn gives grandparents sensible, step-by-step, concrete guidelines on how to participate in the birth and enhance the family experience at this special time. Written in an easy-to-read and sensitive manner the author ranges over a wide variety of subjects that inform, assist and instruct grandparents on how to be both witness and participant in the birth of their grandchild. Of special note is the author's warm, loving advice on handling the birth of a stillborn child that I have not seen addressed elsewhere. I recommend this book to all grandparents and to present and future parents who would like their own parents to be part of the experience of a lifetime."

Arthur Kornhaber M. D.
President and Founder
The Foundation for Grandparenting

Advance Praise Continued

"As the mother of a "preemie" 24 years ago, and a recent grandmother, I very much enjoyed reading, *Attending Your Grandchild's Birth*, and learning about the things I had missed. Now, I understand how I could have been much more help and support for my daughter and daughter-in-law, if this book had been available to me earlier. I hope to have a chance at "grandmotherhood" again, and this time, I'll be prepared."

Charlotte Binder,
Mother, Grandmother, Teacher, Ret. School Librarian

For my grandchildren, Leif Erik, Joseph, Laura, Thomas and Andrew and my children, John, Christine, Jolie and Robert with much love.

Foreword

While I was a family doctor I delivered many babies. During that time, now almost forty years ago, I began to allow family members to be involved, as appropriate, in the birth. That's when I learned that a new baby can cement and affirm family bonds, and when I learned that every time a baby is born, a new grandparent is born too.

For many years I have urged all three generations to participate in the joy and wonder of birth. Rarely has anyone described this less than a wondrous experience. But many grandparents are hesitant about attending their grandchild's birth. They ask many questions about the "how," "why" and "when" of getting involved. Happily, there are answers for grandparents with questions.

In *Attending Your Grandchild's Birth*, author Carolynn Bauer Zorn gives grandparents sensible, step-by-step, concrete guidelines on how to participate in the birth and enhance the family experience at this special time. Written in an easy-to-read and sensitive manner the author ranges over a wide variety of subjects that inform, assist and instruct grandparents on how to be both witness and participant in the birth of their grandchild, and the parenthood of their own child.

Of special note is the author's warm, loving advice on handling the birth of a stillborn child that I have not seen addressed elsewhere. I recommend this book to all grandparents and to present and future parents who would like their own parents to be part of the experience of a lifetime.

Arthur Kornhaber, M. D.
President and Founder
The Foundation For Grandparenting

Preface

In the last five years, I have attended the birth of four grandchildren. I eagerly anticipated each opportunity. I couldn't understand why other grandmothers I knew chose not to attend, even though they were invited. Now, after my experiences, I realize their trepidation and I respect their personal decision. This book is designed to help you answer the question, "If invited, would I like to attend my grandchild's birth?"

Childbirth can be one of life's most joyous moments. Your daughter's first birth becomes a rite of passage as she joins you in parenthood. You become a parent-once-removed, a grandparent.

As the mother of four, I expected the births of my grandchildren to be similar to my deliveries in the 60's and 70's. However, childbirth methods have evolved over the last few decades, making the delivery arena a strange land to those of us who have not been there for many years. In addition, it became clear that each birth is unique to the delivering woman; just as witnessing the experience is unique to each person attending the birth.

I feel strongly that grandparents should educate themselves if they plan to attend the birth of their grandchild, just as the birthing couple prepare themselves by attending prenatal classes. A grandparent can and should attend a prenatal class, go on a hospital tour, and meet the doctor attending their daughter or daughter-in-law.

Reading this book will help you decide if you want to be in the delivery room when birth takes place, what you can expect once you are there, and how you can help.

This book is just for you, the grandparent, written by a grandparent. While it is directed primarily at a future grandmother aiding her daughter, since that is the most common occurrence, it applies equally for a grandfather attending the birth of his grandchild and for a daughter-in-law's birth event.

Birthing couples today may comprise many different combinations: the coach may be the baby's father, or not, or the coach may be a life partner, a mother, a grandparent or friend, even the future adoptive parents. In this context, it is almost impossible to be politically correct. A single word doesn't exist to denote every situation, and to cover all family arrangements in each sentence would be cumbersome. So I have used the most common arrangement, a husband and wife having a baby with the husband acting as coach and the grandparent/s attending.

I decided to write this book because of the variety of experiences I had to deal with while attending the birth of four of my grandchildren. I felt if I had had this book before I entered the delivery arena, I would have been better prepared, more helpful, and enjoyed each birth more fully. Here are the birth stories I lived along with my daughter, Christine.

Her first birth ended in a Cesarean section after a long, difficult labor. Although the baby, Leif Erik, was fine, there were moments when I feared my daughter was going to die. I felt helpless and unprepared. This was not the birth I expected. It was unlike any I had experienced. She was given every intervention available, had equipment connected everywhere and still wasn't making appropriate progress according to the staff. I'd never seen as much apparatus in a labor/delivery room as was present during this labor. This probably accounted for part of my anxiety and helplessness. When did childbirth become a serious condition that had to be treated by hordes of equipment? Where had I been? When I was told she had to have a C-Section I was furious. (I didn't know anything about C-sections, although I learned later they now account for about one-fourth of all births.) How did a healthy, young woman delivering her first baby (who was in no distress) become a candidate for a C-Section I wondered. What was going on? Who or what had failed her? Later, I found out the reason she had to have a C-Section was because her doctor didn't do forceps deliveries(which would have assisted the expulsion of the large baby) and she had not delivered the baby in the time schedule they allowed, so she was diagnosed with "failure to progress." At times she was in severe pain and I agonized over my inability to "fix it."

Her second delivery was of a full term stillborn baby named Joseph. I stayed with her throughout two horrible days of induction, and went into the operating room along with her husband for this tragic, forceps delivery. In my fifty plus years I never knew anyone whose child had been stillborn. I thought stillbirth ceased around the same time covered wagons disappeared. The truth is however, that one percent of all pregnancies end in stillbirth. While we had a trained, caring staff to assist us in the delivery and with our grief process, others aren't so fortunate. I have provided information and help for families faced with this situation or other sad birth outcomes so they will have immediate resources if needed.

My daughter's third delivery was a scheduled induction at 38 weeks. This was the birth of my third grandchild, Thomas. Due to the previous stillbirth, she was advised to have the baby induced early and not wait for spontaneous labor. After a sad birth outcome, subsequent births are fraught with fear, and this one was no exception. My daughter worried about her health, her baby's health and was still struggling with the helplessness she felt to impact her own destiny. While this delivery was extremely mechanized and orchestrated, it was, in the end, a beautiful, happy birth which I captured on video tape.

She recently gave birth to a fourth child, Andrew. This delivery was also induced and was very similar to her third delivery experience except without as much anxiety. It was completely orchestrated by drugs, instruments and medical personnel.

Induction is not always the most comfortable way for a woman to deliver because of the intensity of labor and the many invasive measures that are used. A laboring woman is given a window of time in which birth must occur whereas in a natural setting a labor may take several days and still be perfectly normal. Regardless, induction is becoming more common every day due to the advances in pregnancy management. Very few women give birth in a hospital today without the administration of a contraction producing drug called Pitocin.

Toward the end of this fourth delivery during hard labor, I left. I was admittedly having a hard time watching her discomfort, but I also believed she and her husband might want to share this birth alone. I thought my place this time was with the other grandchildren at home. She delivered Andrew within an hour of my leaving. She and her husband had some time together with him before I came back to the hospital for a short visit.

While I feel I offered some support for my daughter and son-in-law during all four births, I was less able to tend to all of our needs than I would have liked. I improvised as each birth process unfolded, trying to determine what help I should offer and what my role should be. Initially, I was convinced I knew all about childbirth and had experienced everything that could possibly happen; after all, I had given birth four times myself. I was wrong. In my ignorance, I didn't realize that watching your daughter give birth is very different than giving birth yourself, no matter what method of birth is selected. In addition, giving birth today is nothing like it was twenty or thirty years ago. The medical drama that unfolded during the births of my grandchildren often left me feeling totally helpless and ignorant. I was also completely unprepared for the emotions that assaulted me as I tried to find a place for myself during the births and a way to cope with the events. I have learned a few things and I would like to share them with you so you will more fully enjoy your grandchild's birth if you attend.

I admit I am biased in some areas because of my experiences. However, I am sure you will find this book helpful and if it promotes discussion between you and your daughter, or prompts you to do further reading then it will have served its purpose--educating you and helping you make a decision about attending your grandchild's birth.

If you decide to attend the birth of your grandchild after reading this book, please take the book with you for reference and support. It is intended to help you be the best you can be on one of the most important and memorable days of your adult life.

> "I really enjoyed my mother in the delivery room with my husband and me. She helped out quite a bit and helped encourage me through delivering our beautiful baby girl. She took some wonderful pictures we'd never have had if it wasn't for her." Bea, mother

"My parents were there when I gave birth to my first child. My mother was the first one to hold the baby." Kathleen, mother

"I held the baby while they made the footprints. The staff and my daughter made me feel very welcome." Phyllis, grandmother

"I could not have done it without my mother. She was great; very strong and supportive. She anticipated all of my needs without hovering. She didn't let it show that she was worried or anything. She let the midwives and my husband run the show pretty much." Sheila, mother

"My mother did not attend our baby's birth. She would have made me far too nervous!" Jossie, mother

"I was present for five of the eight grandchildren's births. It was very relaxed and wonderful. I do not remember much about my own children's births, so it was a real pleasure to witness such a miracle. All grandmothers should experience this, especially if it is her daughter giving birth. I'm glad I was invited." June, grandmother

"To view a birth is to capture a miracle in progress, a personal event that will never be viewed again as each birth is a treasure in itself." Val, a grandmother

Acknowledgments

Where does one begin to thank all the individuals who help along the way?

For starters I would like to thank Sue Holt, my son's new mother-in-law and my new friend for her final edit of my manuscript. In addition, I would like to thank my sister, Charlotte Binder and daughter, Jolie Matedne, for their editing help on previous versions. It has been a long time since I left the classroom. Thank you to my sister-in-law Joanna Zorn for the cervix chart she drew.

My deep appreciation goes to Dr. Susan Taylor for her medical proofing during a time when she was busy with her own book.

To my daughter, Christine Wolsek, her husband Robert, and her doctor, Dr. Michael Bork, I owe a big thanks for their patience and support during my intrusions into their deliveries and for their allowing me to use their pictures. I also appreciate the many individuals on the internet who shared their stories with me for use in this book.

On the road to being published, the kindness that Dr. Arthur Kornhaber, the President and Founder of *The Foundation For Grandparenting*, offered to a struggling author by sending his advance praise (see the Foreword) and promising future promotion of my book on his website, is extraordinary in today's impersonal environment. Thank you seems hardly adequate.

On a daily basis I have to thank the members of the Ventura County Writers Club for their suggestions and support and of course, my husband, Dave, who has always been my biggest fan, even though childbirth is not his favorite dinner discussion topic.

Table of Contents

List of Illustrations

1. Leaving the hospital with my daughter, Christine, in 1968.
2. My daughter, Christine being checked in triage during her first pregnancy in 1993.
3. Taking video pictures at Erik's birth, 1993.
4. Christine and I with my first grandson, Leif Erik, 1993.
5. Christine being comforted by a visit from Erik during the induction of her stillborn baby, Joseph in 1995.
6. Christine and Dr. Bork during the birth of my third grandson Thomas in 1996.
7. Christine in labor with her fourth boy, Andrew in 1998.
8. Christine with Andrew after his birth.

Chapter One
Becoming a Grandparent

Are you about to become a grandparent? By the year 2004 there will be ninety million grandparents in the United States. Whether it is your first or your fifth grandchild, the birth of a grandchild is one of life's most special events. Each grandchild is a unique blend of numerous generations' genes resulting in qualities and traits which are both familiar and new. Your grandchild will be instantly recognizable while being mysteriously novel. These are the characteristics that you will passionately inform strangers about at every opportunity.

Becoming a grandparent, as I mentioned in the preface, is a rite of passage through which your daughter or son truly becomes an adult and you no longer think of them as a dependent. They now have someone depending on them.

Most adults are thrilled at the prospect of becoming grandparents, and if you are reading this book I suspect you are one of them. Grandparents are all ages and the social categorizing of grandparents as old and retired has long since past. Grandparents today are usually still working and are active, vibrant people with full lives apart from their children. They are educated and anxious to explore many different areas of interest. They have a lot to offer their grandchildren.

Even though grandparents have changed, the important role that they play hasn't changed much. Becoming a grandparent is like being a parent, except to a minor power--or as I call it, once removed. You will love and play with grandchildren differently than you did with your own children precisely because you don't have to "be the parent." The time spent with your grandchildren will be special for them and you and generate memories that will be lifelong for you both.

One of the roles you will play with grandchildren is that of mentor and because of a grandchild's emotional attachment to you, lessons you teach will forever stay in their mind. Just ask any child about the person in the family who taught them the most, or who shared the most special memory with them, and it will more than likely be a grandparent. Grandparents are able to create an atmosphere where children can learn and explore without fear of punishment or failure. A grandparent's love is perceived as unconditional and absolute. It has no obligations. Grandparents are thrilled to see their grandchild play in the band and don't care if he is the best clarinet player or the worst. Grandparents, at least in the past, were the only adults with enough time, desire and opportunity to be mentors. That may be changing today, as day care personnel replace grandparents as the secondary caregivers. One hopes that even though grandparents today are busier and often geographically farther from the family than those in previous generations, they will find a way to continue to fulfill their important role.

Grandchildren provide a bridge between generations. You can feel at ease with grandchildren and they with you even when relations with their parents may be strained. Since you're not the parent, you are not responsible for the final outcome of the child. This frees you to be yourself and to enjoy each grandchild individually. It allows grandchildren a neutral zone where they can be themselves. Grandparents often have more hugs to give and time to give them. Researchers have found that physical affection is a vital element in providing the basis for children to establish and sustain strong friendships, happy marriages and a sense of well-being.

Grandparents are the main teachers of culture as they pass down the wisdom of past generations, (or the gossip about Aunt Judy, however you want to look at it!), in a way that the child's parents cannot. They tell stories about long forgotten family events and times. Through their stories they make a child's parents real. This knowledge of family history and traditions, as well as ethnic heritage, is vital to the child's perception of his place in the family and in the universe.

You will be a role model to help teach your grandchildren what "older" people are like. You may be the religious link in the full circle of life for your grandchildren. Grandchildren think grandparents are closer to God because of their age, their nearness to the end of life. Your death will most likely be the first death they will experience, so they will learn from you not only about life, with your stories of their birth and their parents' birth, but also about death. For you, grandchildren provide an affirmation of life's continuation.

Your grandchildren see you as mystical. You have lived in other times and places and have experienced more than anyone else they know. You have been a child, a teenager and a parent. They will come to you to ask questions that they won't ask anyone else because of your vast knowledge and experience.

In all cultures grandparents are perceived to be a sort of nurturer or great parent because of their unique role of being interested in the well being of all parties, the parents as well as the grandchildren. In Norwegian, the word for grandparent is "Beste Mor" or "best mother." The highest form of respect for a Navajo is to call someone "grandfather".

Unfortunately there are some couples who believe they should limit the time their children spend with the grandparents. They may feel their parents are too rigid, too old fashioned, too cranky, too permissive, or too unorthodox. Usually these parents do not have a good relationship with their parents and perhaps were not close to their grandparents either. Thus, they may not understand the vital role grandparents play, regardless of their shortcomings, in the life of a child.

> "I know that while it is important for grandparents to have an active and consistent relationship with their grandchildren, boundaries must be set. I don't see eye-to-eye with either my mother or mother-in-law on child-rearing issues, so limited involvement in certain areas is a must." Vanessa, mother

Being a grandparent will happen, in almost all cases, if you have children. Like the "Grinch" who couldn't stop Christmas from coming, you can't stop the act of becoming a grandparent. Most grandparents revel in the role.

Grandparenting however, deciding what kind of a grandparent you will be, depends on many things. One of the most important things is the quality of your relationship with your son or daughter. This may be the perfect time, as you contemplate your role as a grandparent-to-be, to take the necessary steps toward healing any wound with your children which may prevent you from being involved in the life of your grandchildren. It is a great joy to be the most cherished object in a child's life--a grandparent--and you shouldn't miss a moment of it.

> "We already had a good relationship, but the experience made us even closer, perhaps because we now have shared that miracle of birth that only women can understand." Denese, mother

> "With the same eager anticipation I approached motherhood, I approach grandmotherhood. Having children, raising them to be fine adults and now having grandchildren to teach, enjoy and love, is the essence of a fulfilled life and the greatest accomplishment you will ever have." Lefaine, grandmother.

> "I thought as I held my grandson for the first time how one so little could cause such a line of connection; my son is a father; my daughter is an aunt; I'm a grandfather; my mom is a great-grandmother; the family name will continue for one more generation now." Bob, grandfather.

Chapter Two
Grandparents In The Delivery Room

> "The birth was over six months ago and my
> mother and I speak about the strong bond which
> has formed because of her direct involvement."
> Denise, mother

Today most hospitals allow birthing couples to invite a parent or parents, siblings or others to be present at the birth of a baby. If you have been invited to be present for the birth of your grandchild, let me give you some things to consider.

Being a grandparent is as natural as being a parent. You can't help but love your grandchild. However, the attachment and closeness that you may capture by actually witnessing the birth is a lot like the bonding that parents experience after holding their own newborn.

> "There are no words to express the feeling of
> seeing your grandchild born." Pat, grandmother

> "My granddaughter is twenty months old. I was
> present at her birth. I have never felt anything
> like it in my entire life." Dyana, grandmother

So while it isn't necessary to be at the birth, if you are invited and decide to attend, you will forever be a part of this history making event as the story is told again and again during the next several decades. And your attachment to this grandchild will undeniably be strong.

When becoming a grandparent, the impulse to nurture is reawakened. You will want to "take care of" your daughter from the moment she announces she is expecting a baby. However, in the delivery room her husband will be the main caregiver and decision maker, despite the fact that you have, perhaps, more than a twenty year relationship with her and he has only a few years. This may be the first time in your life that you entrust your daughter's care to someone else. This may even be the first time your daughter is in the hospital. Standing by and watching your child in pain or discomfort and not being able to prevent it can be a very emotional experience. It may be an experience you feel you cannot handle or do not wish to have. Let me help you make a decision about attending your grandchild's birth by providing you with information and sharing birth stories.

> "My mother attended my daughter's birth, (coincidentally in the same hospital where she delivered me thirty-two years earlier)and it was wonderful. Not every mother is suitable for that situation." Rika, mother

> "I was very glad to have my mother there with my husband because she helped him keep calm as well as helped keep me calm. She was companion, nurse, masseuse and friend." Jennifer, mother

Through your daughter, you will relive the experiences you had during the birth of your children. You may think that you know what to expect since, after all, you have had at least one child before. However, your birth experience will not be the same as your daughter's birth experience. So you must be prepared to open your mind and do some preparation prior to the birth. The childbirth experience for each person and for each delivery is different and brings with it its own set of circumstances. No two deliveries are the same. So if you had an unpleasant birth in the past you may need to put it aside and anticipate a story-book birth now; if you previously had a glorious birth experience, you need to be prepared for the possibility that this birth might be a completely different adventure.

"It was the most wonderful experience. While I cannot be with my daughter for every new event in her life, I wanted to be there for the act of childbirth. There was a feeling of continuity - as I had given birth to her and now she, in turn, was giving birth to another." Denese, grandmother

When you gave birth you knew what to do. The role of a birthing mother, like the role of a bride in a wedding, is pretty well defined even though it may change as birthing arrangements change over time. The role of a grandparent in the delivery room is not well defined, however. This new phenomena of having an additional family member attend a hospital birth is relatively new. Not long ago even a husband wasn't allowed in the delivery room. What will you be doing? What will they allow you to do? What do you want to do? How much will you see and do you think you should?

To help you I have outlined in this book a variety of roles you can assume which will be pleasurable for you and helpful for your daughter and son-in-law.

You can be the photographer, the masseuse, the "go-for", or the baby-sitter for other grandchildren who may be present. If you are close to your daughter you will be able to provide a genuine service, by offering comfort and support along with her husband; if you are not close, this may be the opportunity you need to begin to build a relationship again. You need to decide if you want to attend the birth and, if so, define what you will be doing before you enter the delivery room. The following informative chapters prepare you to make this decision and to enhance your experience.

"We were in the labor room with our daughter-in-law. The experience of being with her in labor and trying somewhat to comfort her was very special to us. Our son and daughter-in-law were thrilled we could share this event with them." Barbara, grandmother

"It demonstrated to me as nothing else ever could how much my daughters loved their father and mother by being willing to share this most wonderful and most private of experiences with us." Carol, grandmother

"I believe the birth of our child is a highly personal and intimate one that I do not care to share with anyone other than my husband. My relationship with my mother is very poor." Vanessa, mother

"I figured she (mom) was with me through puberty so she's seen me at my worst and would probably be more understanding if I got mean than my husband." Sheila, mother

"My mom was there for the birth. I was so glad she was. I didn't have her there for the first son because I was too embarrassed and thought it should just be my husband, but I was wrong. She was so happy and said it was one of the most exciting moments of her life." Leslie, mother

"My mom drove me to the hospital. She sat in a rocking chair off to the side of the room. It seemed natural for her to be there. Through all the commotion she (Mom) sat and rocked quietly and calmly. I think every woman should have the opportunity to witness birth from the passenger's seat." Jacqueline, mother

Chapter Three
During the Pregnancy

Starting with the first phone call announcing her pregnancy, you and your daughter begin planning. While you anxiously await the first ultrasound which will determine the sex of the expected baby and the condition of his or her health, you begin thinking about a room to decorate, a baby shower, the upcoming holiday celebrations, etc.

While I don't want to lay out the entire nine months here since there are plenty of books available for information about pregnancy, I do want to call to your attention a few events in which you may be involved and discuss some new information of which even your daughter may not be aware. In addition, I want to offer some ways that you can help during the pregnancy period while awaiting the actual birth event.

Length of Pregnancy

There have been jokes about pregnancy being ten months not nine as women are led to believe. The length of pregnancy is actually ten *lunar* months. This is ten 28 day cycles or 280 days. So no matter how you figure it, it is slightly longer than nine months.

The Ultrasound

If you can attend your daughter's first ultrasound appointment, (if her husband goes to the first one, perhaps you can attend the next one), it may be possible to know the sex of the upcoming child in advance. I anxiously awaited this information so I could start making the crib blankets and other nursery items in the appropriate colors.

What a marvelous thing--to be able to know if you are going to have a grandson or granddaughter. Well, don't be too sure. In the first place, many couples often don't want to know or want you to know and so the technician withholds the information. This will probably be the first time in this pregnancy that you will have to set aside your desires and respect the desires of your daughter or son. While it is hard for a grandmother to sometimes remember, I know it was for me, this is your daughter's baby and your daughter's pregnancy, not yours.

In many cases, the technician cannot determine with certainty whether the baby is a boy or a girl. Once in awhile even when they determine the sex they are wrong. In the case of my first grandchild the technician could not determine the sex of the fetus. Why, I asked myself, did every other grandmother with whom I talked know the sex of her grandchild and I didn't? The ultrasound's primary purpose is not to give you the sex of the baby, even if it seems to you at the time that it should. Rather, the initial ultrasound determines the length of the pregnancy and firms up the expected due date. It also screens for some birth defects or abnormalities.

Most of the expectant couples today obtain sonogram pictures from their unborn baby's ultrasound scanning procedure and you may be blessed to receive one for your brag book. If you can go to an ultrasound appointment and see the baby move and hear his heartbeat, you will be sharing a special moment with your child and future grandchild that shouldn't be missed. The ultrasound technology is improving every day and the new 3-D technology produces pictures that are very clear.

Many technicians will also allow the couple to have a video tape covering part of the ultrasound procedure if they bring a blank tape to their appointment. This makes exciting viewing at home later and is a treasure to have for posterity. My daughter and I started a video tape of her first child with some ultrasound footage and later added footage at the birth and as he grew up. My son titled the video and added music for us with his computer. (A skill I don't have.) It was enough to make even a seasoned grandparent cry it was so beautiful to watch. As time passed it was of interest to the child also. He will never wonder where he came from.

Morning Sickness and Food

One of the first signs of pregnancy, morning sickness, is now believed to be a natural reaction of the body and serves to protect the developing fetus during a very vulnerable stage. About four out of five women experience nausea during pregnancy. While hormones are believed to initiate the onset of nausea and vomiting that characterize morning sickness, it is this abundance of hormones that also alert the body to the pregnancy condition signaling it to protect the fetus. Cell division and organ development takes place in the first eight to twelve weeks. During this time a fetus is more susceptible to toxins, viruses and drugs. While it is called "morning sickness" it can affect a pregnant woman at any time of the day usually with one part of the day being worse than another.

A pregnant woman's sense of smell is heightened during this time and this also affects her appetite. By causing a woman to avoid eating, or smelling certain foods or chemicals, the body is protecting the unborn fetus. Many women cannot even attend the same functions or do the same activities they enjoyed doing in their pre-pregnant state. For instance, the smell in a gym may keep them from attending basketball games or working out. Even perfume they loved in the past may repulse them now. Their husbands may find out that because of their breath from an earlier lunch of Italian food their kisses are not welcome when they get home.

Most newly pregnant women cannot stand the smell of cigarette smoke. This is a good thing. Even second hand smoke can be harmful and if it causes a smoking woman to quit that is better for her and her baby. Smoking by pregnant women has been linked to a host of health and developmental problems in their offspring including asthma and serious ear infections. A father's smoking affects his semen and is believed to cause his fetus to be more susceptible to immune-system cancers and leukemia. Smoking also transfers nicotine to breast milk. A child born of a smoking mother is more likely to smoke herself. Is this because of an acquired addition to nicotine?

If you or your husband smoke you need to keep in mind that not only is it bad for you and those around you, it is dangerous to the developing fetus. In Finland it's against the law to smoke around a pregnant woman. Try to refrain from smoking around your daughter. If you smoke in the house or car, she may not be able to be in these places until the second trimester. (Pregnancy is broken in three development periods called trimesters, with three months in each trimester.)

A first trimester woman usually has a difficult time cooking because the smell of the food being prepared causes her to feel sick. I used to hold my breath when I went into the kitchen to check on dinner, and then run out closing the door behind me. It's usually a welcome treat if food is brought in, so the cooking is done elsewhere, or if they can afford it, if the expectant parents go out to dinner for awhile. If you invite them over for a meal you should keep in mind that if you cook something like cabbage, which fills the house with its aroma, your daughter may not even be able to stay. Checking with her beforehand may spare hurt feelings.

So what do women with morning sickness eat? Usually bland meals with little fat such as cereal, boiled meats, milk products, fresh fruit, fresh juices (no canned taste), vegetables with little taste like lettuce or peas. Well cooked eggs are usually tolerated. I lived on hot cereal and toast for many weeks when I was pregnant with my first child and for me morning sickness was in the evening. Many women need soda crackers to calm their stomachs before rising each morning. In most women their natural supply of nutrients built up before pregnancy will sustain them until morning sickness passes. They will be encouraged to take a multivitamin tablet by their doctor as soon as pregnancy is confirmed. The fetus is only the size of a peanut so it doesn't need much nourishment. If sickness lasts more than a few months or is so severe that nothing can be kept down, then the doctor may suggest hospitalization so that an IV can be started. While these cases are uncommon they do happen in about three percent of all pregnancies.

There are some foods that should be avoided during early pregnancy because of possible toxins. Large amounts of bitter vegetables such as spinach and broccoli may actually be harmful. Most pregnant women won't desire them so that is usually not a problem. In nature, the bitter taste is there to ward off would be predators and protect the plants' ability to reproduce. We have learned, as a species, over many, many years, to eat only plants that are not toxic to us in the amounts we consume. But even plants and herbs you believe are harmless, such as pepper or basil can be deadly if consumed in large quantities. To err on the safe side, a woman should eat only what she feels like eating such as well cooked boiled meats, peeled and well cooked vegetables in small quantities, and peeled fresh fruits and dairy products, cereals and breads.

Barbecued meat, with its burnt exterior, will probably send a newly pregnant woman to the bushes to throw up, so grilling and barbecuing might be better tolerated later in pregnancy. It is well known that the barbecued black outside of meat is toxic.

It is interesting to note that high doses of Vitamin A can be toxic, also. For this reason, serving liver, which naturally contains large amounts of this vitamin, should be avoided. Here again, it is doubtful if a first trimester woman wants to eat liver, but chilled pate' might be disguised enough with spices and crackers that it would be appealing. Chilling a food disguises its smell and taste and makes it more appetizing during this period of pregnancy. If you are interested in reading more about morning sickness, there is an excellent book available called, "Protecting Your Baby-to-Be; Preventing Birth Defects in the First Trimester" by Margie Profet.

Other Foods

There are a few foods that should never be eaten by a pregnant woman. Soft white and blue veined cheeses like Brie and Feta may be contaminated with the listeria bacteria and therefore unsafe. Listeria may also be found in undercooked beef, pork and chicken, leftovers, and cold cuts and hot dogs. While the bacteria isn't as common as salmonella or E.coli, the percentage of people who die from it is higher. One out of every five cases is fatal. Approximately 9,000 people a year die of food born disease in the United States. The bacteria infection listeriosis in the mother can cause miscarriage and stillbirth. Meats need to be cooked thoroughly or not eaten. Vegetables should be washed thoroughly before eating because the bacteria is also found in the soil. Recently alfalfa sprouts have been linked to outbreaks of salmonella and E. coli. Since they are hard to wash thoroughly maybe they should be avoided.

Potatoes, especially their skins, are full of toxins and should probably be avoided altogether by a pregnant woman in her first trimester.

So when you invite your daughter over for dinner don't serve Greek salad with Feta cheese. And if she is in the first trimester don't serve baked potatoes with barbecued chicken and broccoli and herb salad with fresh basil. Pungent, bitter vegetables and herbs as well as onions, garlic and peppers are full of toxins and probably unappealing to her.

Since fruits are meant to be eaten so their seeds can be spread and prosper, nature has made them sweet and less toxic than vegetables. Fruit salad with cottage cheese, and fruit coolers with yogurt may be appealing.

Macaroni and cheese, custards, rice and simple pasta dishes, turkey and bread might be better offerings. Cold, salty, sweet and even sour foods are better handled overall and safer than fatty, hot, bitter or spicy foods.

Morning sickness usually is more severe in the first pregnancy so subsequent pregnancies will probably be easier on everyone, but the toxic rules still apply. Staying with bland food, fewer vegetables and herbs, boiled or microwaved meat, and plenty of fruits is the wiser path for a pregnant woman in her first trimester.

Nausea can often be relieved by applying acupressure at the Nei-Kuan acupuncture point. This point is on the inside of the wrist between the two tendons and about three finger-widths from the crease where the wrist joints the hand. There are over the counter wrist pressure bracelets or wristbands which operate on this principle. They are reported to be effective in sixty percent of the cases of nausea.

Car trips

Riding in the car or flying may bother a newly pregnant woman more than it ever did before and exacerbate her nausea. If you are planing to invite her on a outing, allow her to sit in the front seat and make it a short trip. If she does not feel like flying to visit you in another city, be sensitive to her condition. Suggest she might rather visit during her second trimester. Flying is usually not recommended for the third trimester.

Alcohol

Alcohol consumption is dangerous for pregnant women. While it was not known that alcohol could be dangerous to the developing fetus when I was pregnant in the 60's and 70's, it is widely recognized as a harmful substance today. Alcohol is a major cause of birth defects. Several thousand cases of fetal alcohol syndrome occur in the United States each year. While wine, because it contains the natural tannins from grapes, may be repulsive to a first trimester woman, other alcoholic drinks may not. If you are serving dinner for your daughter, remember she should not be drinking. Suggesting you meet for cocktails would probably not be the appropriate afternoon outing or politically correct.

As pregnancy progresses, all foods should be better tolerated and toward the end of pregnancy food cravings may appear. I wanted coconut ice cream with a passion. I ate so much of it that it was many years before I could eat it again. While there is no proof that food cravings during pregnancy are a protective mechanism, I don't believe they are simply a desire for attention either. There is probably some as yet unknown reason they occur. And despite the pickles and ice cream jokes, most women crave very different foods.

Needed Foods

One of the vitamins pregnant women need to consume is folic acid or folate. It has been proven that deficiencies of this nutrient cause neural tube defects like spina bifida. This condition affects about one percent of newborns. It's so critical that pregnant women need to have adequate amounts of folic acid before they even become pregnant to prevent this birth defect. Good sources of folic acid are Romaine lettuce, citrus juice or fruit, pinto beans, cantaloupe, avocados, egg yolks, tomatoes and cereal or grains. All of these items should be appealing to a newly pregnant woman. B-12 is needed along with the folic acid. While it is usually obtained from animal products, fortified cereals and vitamin supplements can supply a first trimester women's needs during the time in which animal products may not be well tolerated. Vegetarians may need to supplement their diet so that they obtain adequate amounts of folic acid. (You will benefit from eating more of these items yourself, because foods high in folate reduce the blood concentrations of an amino acid, homocysteine. High Homocysteine levels have been linked to an increased risk for a heart attack or stroke.)

Adequate Vitamin C in both the mother and father is believed to be necessary to prevent DNA damage. If both the mother and father have appropriate levels of vitamin C before conception occurs, it is believed the healthy sperm and egg will be less susceptible to DNA damage during the massive cell division that occurs in early pregnancy. It is also thought that smoking by either party prior to pregnancy may predispose the vulnerable cells of the fetus to DNA damage. Adequate vitamin C may help offset this effect.

It appears that taking vitamin C and E during pregnancy may also reduce the incidence of preeclampsia. Preeclampsia is a condition that affects about five percent of pregnant women, usually first time mothers, and is characterized by high blood pressure, excessive swelling and abnormal placenta development. It can be life threatening to the expectant mother as well as her fetus. As with DNA damage, it is the oxygen-free radicals that appear to cause the problems so adding vitamin C, which is an antioxidant that removes the free radicals, may help prevent this condition. A recent study suggests that increased levels of calcium may also serve a role in preventing preeclampsia. Teenage mothers, mothers over forty, women carrying twins and women who work (no matter where they work) are also more likely to suffer from this condition. The cause is still not fully understood and no treatment works for everyone. Delivery of the baby is the best solution if the condition becomes severe.

Tears of Pregnancy

Do you remember crying for no reason when you were pregnant? Here again, the hormones released during pregnancy most likely trigger the unexplained crying episodes as a way of protecting the fetus from anxiety and toxins. Tears it turns out are another way nature eliminates toxins, so even tears of joy may be a response by nature to cleanse the system. A good cry also relieves tension and restores a feeling of well being. So be patient with your daughter and allow her to cry because she probably needs to. Nature is at work. We do not understand all the processes of the human body and our evolutionary responses yet, but, in the meantime, I believe we should trust our bodies more than we do and educate ourselves as much as possible.

Hot Tubs

Elevated body temperatures pose significant health threats to unborn infants. During early pregnancy they have been associated with an increased risk of birth defects like spina bifida. When planning events, keep this in mind if you are planning a hot tub party. It wouldn't be fair if your daughter or daughter-in-law is the only one who must remain on the sidelines.

Cats

Toxoplasmosis is common in domestic cats and they transmit the disease to humans through their feces. Approximately one percent of the babies in North America are born with this infection even though we have known of the danger for a long time. A pregnant woman should stay away from a cat's litter box and should wash her hands thoroughly after touching a cat or digging in soil that may have been contaminated by a cat. If she already has a cat, she may have had the infection already (symptoms are vague--resembling mononucleosis) and although she can be infected again, a re-infection is not as likely to be transmitted to her fetus. If you own a cat perhaps it would be better if your daughter visited you at her house or at a restaurant.

(Toxoplasmosis can also be found in undercooked pork, beef or chicken.)

Swimming

Swimming in public pools is usually considered safe during pregnancy, however swimmers may be infected by contaminated pool water. Enterovirus infections, which can be a result of swimming in a public pool can be life-threatening to the fetus in the third trimester according to Dr. Raymond Poliakin's book, *What You Didn't Think to Ask Your Obstetrician.* Hepatitis A can also be contracted from a contaminated pool. Lake swimming can expose our daughter and her fetus to many diseases, bacteria and parasites. Have your lake water checked for Leptospirosis, Giardiasis, and Amebiasis if you live on a lake. Swimming in lakes maybe should be avoided, and swimming in pools limited to private backyard pools only where you have more control over the condition of the water.

Drugs

Your daughter will be advised what she may or may not take by her doctor, such as aspirin (which may impair fetal heart development) and Tylenol and allergy medication. You may have been her source of medical advise when she was sick in the past, but even if you are a doctor, you must now encourage her to heed only the recommendations of her obstetrician if she is sick during her pregnancy.

Due to the explosion of birth defects in the 1950's after the drug Thalidomide was used, doctors have been more conscious of the dangers of drugs on the developing fetus. They are kept up to date on drug testing and the appropriateness of new drugs for use by pregnant women.

Eye glasses and contacts

During pregnancy eyes retain more water. Since this changes their contours ophthalmologists are often able to determine whether a woman is pregnant just by examining her eyes. For this reason, pregnancy is not the time for new glasses to be purchased. If your daughter is considering obtaining a new prescription remind her to check with her doctor first.

Weight Gain

While pregnant women like to say they are eating for two, in the first weeks this is not true. Ninety percent of the baby's weight gain occurs after the fifth month of pregnancy--fifty percent of this in the last two months. So in the first trimester, a healthy woman is not eating for two and does not need a lot of extra calories. After being all over the scale from 1950 to 1990, the accepted total weight gain during pregnancy, according to the Institute of Medicine of the National Academy of Sciences, is now twenty-five to thirty-five pounds. The mother's weight at the time she gives birth and the size of the baby have very little to do with each other. So don't push food when you are visiting with your daughter or comment on her weight gain if she is getting fat. This matter is best left to her doctor. She will listen to him whereas she might be upset if you comment one way or the other.

Clothing

An average woman's waistline will double during pregnancy. Your daughter may be eager to shop for maternity clothes or she may not want to wear them at all, but one thing is for sure, she will never be prepared for how much her body will change. She can look at pictures in books and at other pregnant women and still not imagine how her phycial dimensions will change until she has been pregnant at least once. If you get the opportunity, you should shop with her a couple times and remind her that some things she wants to purchase will not fit later in pregnancy. Although some women say they can still wear their jeans (unzipped) with a large shirt, I can't believe they are comfortable. I have found it helps to buy a few things in the second trimester and then in the third trimester buy a few more. In suggesting this to your daughter you can point out that she will be sick of the old clothes and will probably need a larger size for the new ones. If you sew you could offer to sew some maternity clothes for her.

In Summary

Entertaining your pregnant daughter may not be as simple as it was in the past, but protecting your future grandchild is important. Discuss the items I mention in this section with your daughter and see what her pregnancy books say. Ask her what her doctor thinks. It can be an opportunity to show her you are interested in her pregnancy and are still concerned about her if done appropriately. In summary, be sensitive to your daughter's needs and special considerations during her days of pregnancy and enjoy this time as much as she does.

Chapter Four
Birth Options Today

There are many different places for your daughter or daughter-in-law to give birth today. Before you make a decision about attending the birth, you will probably want to know what it will be like. Will the birth take place in the hospital, in a birthing center or at home? What is the difference between these birth settings? What kind of a birth does your daughter expect and what birth plan has she outlined?

To review the birth options today, we must quickly review what the childbirth experience was in the past, perhaps for you.

Although childbirth is a natural, biological, and physiological process, it is not completely instinctual. In past cultures, a woman giving birth learned from other women what to expect and what to do. She was assisted by women with wisdom and experience handed down from generation to generation. Some of this informal education still occurs today by the telling of "birth stories."

But more information is required today by women giving birth in most industrialized nations than can be obtained from their mother or grandmother, because the birthing process has changed so dramatically.

Prior to 1900, home birth with a midwife was the accepted practice. It was a family event with female relatives aiding the birthing mother and caring for her during her "confinement." Confinement required a pregnant woman to remain at home during most of her pregnancy and for birth.

By 1936, seventy-five percent of births took place in a hospital. Hospital birth had become "fashionable." The move from the home to the hospital was fueled by the promise of pain relief. This pain relief initially was a triple drug approach called "twilight sleep", which incorporated a shot of morphine at the beginning of labor, followed by the administration of amnesiac scopolamine during the middle of labor and the breathing of chloroform or ether during the baby's passage through the birth canal. The mother was semi-conscious throughout the process and therefore was strapped to the bed. Although her body felt the pain, and she may have cried out, she did not remember any of it. She awoke hours later in her room, after a brief stay in the recovery room. The nurse told her whether she had a girl or a boy, since her baby was already in the nursery and her husband, who had been sent home earlier, may not have arrived back at the hospital yet. Some of you may have experienced this type of birth; I did.

I remember how uncomfortable and frightened I was when they sent all my clothes home with my husband after I was admitted and put on a hospital gown. I was given an enema and then left alone to struggle to get my elephant-sized body down from the bed and rush to the bathroom time and time again. No one was around to help me.

I don't remember much else except waking up in the recovery room and being told I had had a boy. No one could, including me, understand my apathy toward this new baby. I didn't entirely believe he was mine--I hadn't seen or felt him being born.

My throat was so sore I could hardly talk. Later I found out that this was because I had screamed through the entire labor, on my back, tied down. I didn't remember it, but I was mortified at finding out. I was determined that if I ever had a baby again, it would be different. I had numerous stitches and a forceps delivery since I was unable to assist. I could not sit comfortably for weeks due to the huge, painful hemorrhoids. This birth was macabre, lonely and impersonal. There was no possibility of bonding and no comfort from my husband.

Along with the introduction of anesthesia, childbirth required that women become surgical patients, lying down with arm restraints and leg stirrups, prepared for "the operation" with the aid of enemas and pubic shaving. Because women were unable to help with the delivery of their baby (due to the drugs and restraints), they needed doctors to assist with the birth. Doctors then found they needed forceps and episiotomies to complete the delivery. Although doctors who specialized in delivering babies were now called "obstetricians", from the Latin meaning *to stand by*, they didn't just stand by to catch the baby any longer, but instead they felt it was their job to deliver the woman *of* her baby. Women, with their body directing them, no longer delivered their babies; their babies were extracted from them. Birth had become a pathological process requiring medical help.

> "I was drugged…(during birth)…the last thing I remember was being put to sleep and when I woke up my husband told me we had a daughter. My first two deliveries were frightening and if it weren't for the outcome(a wonderful baby) I think I would have been too afraid to ever have a second or third." Pat, grandmother

> "I felt like I had been cheated during her(daughter's) birth as things were done differently in the 60's." Denese, mother

Over the next forty years, women began questioning whether birth was meant to be a medical event and whether these practices were for their good or for the convenience of the hospital staff. Expectant mothers educated themselves about their bodies and about the childbirth process. They demanded that their husbands be allowed in the delivery room. They soon found natural alternatives to heavy anesthesia for pain relief through Dr. Robert Bradley's, *Husband Coached Childbirth*, Grantly Dick-Read's, *Childbirth Without Fear* and the writings of a French obstetrician named Fernand Lamaze. The women of the late 60's and early 70's were not shy in demanding reform, as history reminds us. They embraced a natural approach to their bodies that included more natural childbirth experience. They wanted to be awake and remember the childbirth event.

It was during this time that two types of spinal anesthesia, the saddle block, and the caudal anesthesia (which causes less paralysis than a saddle block) became popular. If you had your children in a hospital in the 70's you probably had this type of medication, which, while removing the pain, also numbed the entire lower half of the body. It allowed a woman to be awake and see the birth, but not to participate much.

My second child was born after the administration of a saddle block in 1968. Even though I could feel no labor contractions (I had driven myself to the hospital) and didn't want it, I was told I had to have it--it was hospital policy.

Before the end of the 70's a plethora of women demanded even less medical intervention and a more natural birth setting. Home births were on the rise again.

Hospitals slowly began to offer an alternative to the standard hospital birth in the form of an "alternate birthing center"(or "family birthing center" or "24 hour suite") to avoid losing these future patients. This center, while located in or attached to the hospital, was available to low risk mothers and offered a more natural birth setting. The birthing rooms were large and "home-like". Unwelcome procedures such as pubic shaving and enemas were eliminated. Family members, especially the husband/coach, were welcome to attend the birth. Even though these centers were a step forward, they still included interventions such as the intravenous drip of glucose solution, fetal monitors and artificial rupture of the membranes. Some of these family birthing centers still operate today.

Childbearing centers, which were similar but free standing and financially independent, offered an even calmer birth setting. Very few drugs were encouraged. While a doctor attended the birth, the majority of the labor was under the supervision of the birthing staff, (usually a nurse/midwife) with help from the mother and her family. Everyone worked as a team to keep the mother comfortable, relaxed and under control with minimal intervention and little or no pain medication. The baby was allowed to enter the world in his or her own time. Freestanding birth centers offered reduced costs, freedom to eat and drink and almost unlimited birthing positions and unlimited visitors at the birth. If any crisis requiring intervention arose, the patient was immediately transferred to the nearest hospital.

Many of you probably had your babies during this transition period between the traditional hospital birth and the birthing center deliveries. I delivered my third child in a hospital with traditional labor and delivery rooms, but was allowed some flexibility by my doctor. Because my doctor respected my desires, I was able to decline an IV, the breaking of my water, pubic shaving, enema and an internal fetal monitor. I had a completely natural(drug free)delivery requiring only a couple of pushes. I was allowed to nurse my baby immediately after the birth in the hallway on my gurney.

My fourth and last child born in 1978, would have been born at home if he had not been hung up in the birth canal. I labored all evening, taking a long bath, shaving my legs, packing my bag. After I started to get uncomfortable I woke my husband and we called a neighbor to baby-sit the other children. I remember thinking as I walked to the car, barely able to walk, that we were told in birth preparation class that if you couldn't walk you were ready. Indeed I was fully dilated when I was checked upon admittance at the hospital. I was sent immediately to the delivery room, but after my doctor arrived and determined the baby was hung up, he insisted I have a caudal so he could turn the baby. My son was born quickly thereafter. I had wanted to have this baby and return home immediately but ended up staying overnight. A stand-alone birthing center located next to this hospital opened the next year.

In the 1970's the electronic fetal monitor, EFM, was introduced and with it, most likely because of it, the Cesarean rate accelerated from five percent to thirty percent in the next twenty years. The fetal monitor, by being able to alert the doctor when the baby is in distress, allowed him not only the opportunity to intervene and possibly avoid harm to the infant, it almost demanded he intervene or be faced with a lawsuit later if for some reason the baby was born with problems. Unfortunately, the monitor is only a machine made by man and it can malfunction or be misinterpreted by the staff. As a result, many of the Cesarean sections which were performed may have been unnecessary. It is unlikely that suddenly twenty-five percent more babies were in distress than in the previous decades, especially with the improvements in prenatal care, testing, and nutrition.

The debate continues about the justification for the high Cesarean rate in the United States. It appears that as fetal monitors have improved and training of the staff has improved with widespread use, fewer unnecessary Cesarean sections are occurring. The rate is finally beginning to drop. Since the cost of this surgery is expensive, managed health care may also be a factor in the declining Cesarean rates. With all the technical intervention used today, including fetal monitors, the United States still "has one of the highest cesarean rates in the developed world and one of the worst infant mortality rates" according to John Robbins in his book, *Reclaiming Our Health*. It makes one wonder about "progress."

In the 1980's and 90's pain relief was usually managed with a combination of education, to help women manage their labor pain, and epidural anesthesia, which allows pain relieving medication to be administered when needed while still permitting the birthing woman to feel some sensation and movement. If you talk to mothers today it would seem the epidural has become the "Camelot" drug. Today a majority of women routinely attend some type of birth preparation class, but a majority of class time is now spent on learning about the new technology and drugs, rather than on how to manage labor naturally.

Hospitals replaced the traditional labor room, delivery room and recovery rooms with a single birthing room, or delivery suite, called an LDR (Labor Delivery Recovery). The first one opened in 1969. These rooms ensure that the delivering woman does not have to be moved during her labor and delivery, and provide a comfortable alternative to a standard hospital room. LDRs attempt to duplicate the atmosphere of the home birth or a birthing center birth by offering many of the same features such as home entertainment centers and whirlpool tubs. These rooms are well decorated and keep most of the equipment out of sight until needed. As the birth progresses more and more of the tools of the trade appear. After the birth, the baby is examined, cleaned and weighed in the same room and returned to the parents for a bonding period during which time the mother may nurse.

Most hospitals have many of these birthing suites and couples today will more than likely deliver their baby in one, rather than at home or in a free standing birthing center, even though hospital births have never been proven to be substantially safer for healthy mothers expecting a normal delivery.

There is a comeback recently of midwife attended births both in a home birth and birthing center setting. Many obstetricians have a midwife on their staff as a choice for patients who wish to use one. These midwives are overseen by the physician.

With the new interest in midwives, home births are also enjoying a comeback and not just with lower income families living in sparsely populated areas. Many educated, professional couples are choosing to deliver their baby at home under the care of a midwife with their entire family in attendance. Depending on which book or report you read, home birth may be said to be as safe as hospital births or not nearly as safe. There certainly is no chance of baby switching or kidnapping with a home birth and home births have a much lower rate of infection.

Doulas or birth attendants are also being used today to accompany the birthing woman through her labor and delivery in tandem with the doctor. Doulas, (from the Greek "in service of") are hired as professional labor assistants. They help with comfort measures, and offer support and encouragement during the birth process. In the future, doulas may replace the husband as the birth assistant for the delivering woman, allowing the husband relief from all the current expectations and responsibilities so he can enjoy the birth as a companion to his beloved.

Today, with the availability of the synthetic oxytocin drip, Pitocin(which causes contractions of the uterus and helps dilation of the cervix), and prostaglandin gel (used to soften and ripen the cervix for the start of labor), chemically controlled labor is routine in most hospital births, both in the LDRs and in old fashioned labor and delivery rooms. With this scripted labor comes a highly mechanized delivery with constant monitoring, electronic dials, equipment with printouts and beepers, needles, tubes and bottles. As the woman's labor progresses, more and more equipment will appear to decorate her and her room. The expectant mother might look as if she is in intensive care with all of this equipment. It may look very frightening to you.

As you discuss the upcoming birth of your grandchild with your daughter, listen to her birth plan as she attends birth education classes and goes on the hospital tour. The closer she gets to her delivery date, the more defined her desires will become. Don't be surprised if she is planning on pain management and intervention as described in the preceding paragraph, because it is pretty standard today. Remember, this is her birth and her body. Her and her husband's desires are to be respected. It is probably safe to say that much of what she will be experiencing during her delivery will be foreign to you. You may never have chosen this type of intervention for yourself, but let me assure you that many women enjoy this managed, medical birth experience completely and wouldn't have it any other way.

I enjoyed the natural birth process and preferred to feel my baby and participate in the birth than to feel needles and give up control and mobility. I was sort of an "earth mother" in my day. Besides wanting as little intervention as possible, I wanted to leave the hospital as soon as possible. I never stayed longer than forty-eight hours during a time when the average stay was three days.

However, my daughter didn't want to feel anything if she didn't have to and was very accepting of the interventions that an epidural delivery prompted.

If your daughter originally desired a more drug free birth and circumstances demanded a change to her birth plan, she will feel disappointed and need your support even more.

With the knowledge I will give you of the birth protocol used in most hospitals today; you will be less frightened and more helpful.

"No matter what kind of birth it is, it is like an explosion within you with the realization that your child's child is taking its first breath." Pat, grandmother

Chapter Five
A Typical Delivery Room (LDR)

As discussed in the last chapter, the most common delivery room used is an LDR Unit or LDRP (Labor, Delivery, Recovery, Postpartum) Unit. Sometimes they are called birthing rooms even though more than the actual birth takes place in them. Each hospital will explain what their room options are during the hospital tour. Most hospitals have several LDR units and most expectant mothers hope one will be available when they arrive in labor. They are assigned on a first come basis. Hospitals are adding more LDR units all the time because of their popularity. Sometimes women will resort to all kinds of tricks to make sure they get the "good room."

A laboring woman must be well along in her first stage of labor with consistent contractions and usually dilated to 3cm or more before being assigned to an LDR. This decision is made by the hospital or her doctor. Since the idea is not to have to move her again, the staff want to be sure she is going to have the baby within twelve hours or so. Otherwise, the room will be tied up and unavailable for others to use in a reasonable period of time.

The LDR looks like a delightful hotel room with wallpaper and pictures on the wall. The room is well decorated with a private bathroom which may include a whirlpool tub. The entertainment center contains a TV, stereo and often a CD player. Extra tables and chairs are available for visiting family members. A special hospital bed, called a "birthing bed," is used for the entire labor and delivery. It can be reconfigured easily to allow for stirrups and has adequate room for the doctor at the end of the bed. The room contains subdued lighting, which can be adjusted throughout labor, and also has large lights that extend out from the ceiling for the actual delivery. Oxygen equipment and other items lurk behind the bed in a concealed cupboard. A table in the room contains medical equipment which is kept out of sight until the delivery is imminent. Also in the room is an IV stand with an infusion pump, a portable unit fetal heart monitor. The room may contain a sink and cupboard area for hand washing and storage of linens. In the bathroom there are towels, a bath mat and a shower with a seat or stool. Husbands are encouraged to bring swimming trunks so they can help their wives in the shower if she decides to labor there. The hospital also provides a lounge chair and/or a rocker for the coach. There is a night stand, a telephone and an intercom. On one side of the room is an area for the baby which contains a Lucite crib or warming unit beneath which equipment needed for the baby is stored (diapers, alcohol, gauze, measuring tape, eye drops and tee-shirts). Here the infant is examined, cleaned up, weighed and measured, etc., while the new father or coach watches and helps. The purpose is to keep the new family together for the first hour after birth.

The rooms are usually large enough for two nurses, a doctor (and sometimes a resident too), the birthing woman and her husband and at least one guest, the grandmother. Each hospital will have its own guidelines as to how many individuals may be in the room. Sometimes siblings or children and both sets of parents are present.

While this is the most common and popular hospital delivery room today, some hospitals may still have separate labor rooms or delivery rooms and their use would be explained on a hospital tour.

The choice of which room is assigned to a delivering woman may also be determined by her planned hospital stay. If she is planning to leave the hospital as soon as possible, then she may be assigned a different room than if she is there for an induction or scheduled C-section and expects a longer stay. Again, a hospital tour and discussion with your daughter may prepare you for where you will actually be if you come for the delivery. If an LDR unit is not available and the nurses say you cannot stay for the birth because your daughter's hospital room is too small, ask to speak with her doctor and obtain his permission. He is able to make exceptions in hospital policies if he feels compelled to do so. Don't abandon your daughter at the first roadblock without seeking a reasonable resolution if you both feel strongly about your being there.

> "Attending the natural births of my grandchildren has to be the most profound experience of my life. Never did my daughters look so beautiful and never was I more proud of them. The joy and love present in the birthing room defies description." Carol, grandmother

> "I thought it was truly a bonding experience for both my mother and myself. If you are extremely close to whomever you have in the room with you, it will be a wonderful experience for all." Susan, mother

No matter what room your grandchild is delivered in, it can still be a wonderful, rewarding experience.

.

Chapter Six
Hospital Tour/Meeting the Doctor

"I wish I had spent more time preparing myself"
Denese, mother

Most hospitals offer tours of their labor and delivery areas. Your daughter will be encouraged to attend one of these tours by her childbirth education instructor and her doctor. In some cases, the doctors have their own tours set up at the hospital for their patients.

You should go on one of these tours either with your daughter, on your own, or with your husband. A tour just for grandparents is offered along with a grandparenting class at some hospitals. Your daughter may wish to go on the tour twice, once with her husband/coach and once with you. The time you spend with her on this tour offers an opportunity to discuss what your role will be if you attend the birth. Often, being in the birthing arena spurs a mother-to-be to express wishes for her birthing experience which she has not mentioned before. Even if you decide not to attend the birth, the hospital tour is a fun way to share an evening with your daughter and familiarize yourself with the hospital where she will be confined. It will make it much easier if you know in advance where the labor and delivery areas are, and where to park, as well as the visiting hours and rules. You can then advise the rest of the family.

A typical tour is hosted by a labor/delivery nurse. She meets the expectant parents (and family members) in the lobby or in an assigned room. Usually there is a brief lecture or slide show/movie, followed by a walking tour. The tour will showcase an LDR Unit, the nursery, any other available room options, and the operating room where a C-Section could be performed if necessary. The nurse will point out the waiting rooms for guests, discuss visiting hours, hospital policy, nursery practices, and other general information. This same type of tour is offered by birthing centers.

Listen carefully as the nurse relays standard hospital policy and practices. If you or your daughter do not like what you hear, you need to have a private discussion with the nurse after the tour. In addition, your daughter should discuss her individual issues of concern with her doctor.

Nearly all hospital policies can be amended if the doctor requests it! This is one of the important things you and your daughter or daughter-in-law need to remember. The doctor has the final say on just about everything. No one will tell you that, but he is the one who can make things happen. So when you hear hospital policy, think of it as, "ordinary procedures." They may or may not be compatible with your daughter's delivery desires and may often be amended with her doctor's support. After all, the patient is the customer. The doctor wants his patients to be happy with their delivery so they will come back, and the hospital wants the patient to recommend them to others.

Encourage your daughter to be assertive, and not to be intimidated by her doctor or the hospital staff. Most women today do assume a more informed and leading role than they did as a passive, unconscious patient in the past. You however, as the grandmother, must be accommodating to everyone and temper your assertiveness.

During early labor your daughter's doctor may not be at the hospital. He will be phoning the doctor/resident on duty for progress reports and giving instructions to him/her for care based on what information he/she receives. Your daughter may ask to speak to the doctor by phone herself to confirm his instructions or clear up any directions from the hospital staff with which she does not agree.

Let me point out here some information about teaching versus non-teaching hospitals. A teaching hospital has residents. These are doctors who have finished medical school and are training for a certain specialty. They are under the supervision of the "attending physician," (the private doctor). An Intern is a first year resident and a chief resident is a fourth year resident. The job of a resident is to follow a private doctor's patients until he arrives at the hospital.

A non-teaching hospital will not have residents nor students. In a non-teaching hospital patients will be examined by the doctor on duty until their attending (private) physician arrives.

A patient in a teaching hospital, however, has the right to refuse to be examined by a resident and may request that only her attending doctor perform any invasive procedures including a pelvic. She also can refuse to be examined too often--such as every hour--or to be examined by several different residents who may come on duty during the course of her labor. Frequent pelvic exams are not needed for most patients in labor. A pelvic exam upon entrance to the labor/delivery unit is to be expected but the patient has some control over the number and spacing of pelvic exams after that and over who performs them. Often it is the nurse who will perform the exams and procedures. A patient has the right to negotiate the amount of times she is disturbed. The attending physician has the final word.

I discuss the above only because patients often think they have to submit to whatever procedure anyone wants to perform, but that is not true. Patients have rights and these rights can be obtained from childbirth preparation organizations.

In a perfect scenario each laboring woman has only one nurse and one doctor attending her throughout delivery. Sometimes the resident, following her care prior to the doctor's arrival, will attend the birth at the request of the attending physician. The primary doctor may also request an additional nurse to help during the actual delivery. If a labor extends past the normal change in shift, then the patient will have more than one nurse. Some hospitals even allow half shift schedules and this could leave a laboring woman with several different nurses in an eight to ten hour time period and each nurse could have different ideas as to how to manage and promote labor. This causes unnecessary distress and confusion to everyone attending the birth. Some nurses will be more receptive to having family members in the room than others and more willing to work with them. Some nurses will develop a closer relationship with the laboring woman by using a hands on approach while others may spend the whole time reading the printout from the monitor as if the woman wasn't even there. I observed this first hand with my daughter's first birth. She was attended by three different nurses and several different residents, each one with a different bed-side manner and idea about labor management.

Your daughter will write a birth plan prior to birth in cooperation with her doctor and depending on her health toward the end of pregnancy. Here is some information about the birth plan. No such thing was even thought of when you and I had our babies. For the most part, we had no say about what happened to us after we passed through the hospital doors. Some argue that writing a birth plan is just wishful thinking and that if it has to change because of complications at delivery it makes the delivering woman feel like a failure. I think birth plans are a good way for a couple to examine more carefully the hospital protocols and completing one will prompt them to ask appropriate questions of both the hospital and the doctor.

Sometimes forms are handed out at birth preparation classes or by the doctor or hospital but one can be made personally by the expectant couple with the cooperation of their doctor. A copy is clipped to the hospital chart and the couple keeps one. If you are going to be at the birth, you might like to have a copy of it. It is not a legal document but a guide for the birth expressing the couple's desires and preferences.

What is on the Hospital Menu and what does the birthing couple want? Do they want something the hospital's not offering? Will it be allowed? Did they get prior approval from their doctor? These are some of the questions which should be part of a birth plan and answered prior to birth.

Example of Birth Plan Topics

Opening Paragraph: The couple's birth philosophy and their degree of preparation. Any special needs or fears and special help they need. How they chose the hospital and or birth attendant.

List of people who will be at the birth: Grandmother to be, attendant such as a Doula, coach, others.

List of Preferences at check-in time: Walking, wheelchair, option to go home if not far enough along.

Preferences for people present: Only want future grandmother in the room during the actual birth, or throughout, husband to be with wife even if a C-Section is required.

Room Preference: LDR, Delivery suite, etc.

Comfort Props: Pillows, hot packs, tennis balls pregnant woman may bring, things hospital will provide, shower/tub, ice, birthing ball, birthing stool.

Birth environment: Want calm, quiet, subdued lighting, few interruptions from staff, examinations infrequently.

Time Limit Preference: Desire to be allowed to labor at own pace, no undue pressure to speed up labor and delivery. Permission to labor longer than 12 hours if necessary if mother and baby are fine. What is the hospital protocol on this? What is the time limit after an epidural is started? What is appropriate rate of dilation in order to avoid a C-Section due to "failure to progress."

Nutritional Needs: Want food to be allowed if labor is prolonged, with ice chips, juice, water and suckers throughout.

Medication Plan: Desired medication from least to most, "natural" or no pain relief, up to an epidural and all the choices in between.

Self help relief: Allow laboring woman to do whatever she feels helps to relieve pain, including, walking, squatting, birth stool, birth ball, bathing or shower, etc.

Concern about intervention: What concerns are for following medical interventions and when they are used –

1) Electronic Fetal Monitoring, internal or external
2) Rupturing of membranes, Natural or artificial (let happen naturally)
3) Vaginal exams, frequent or as necessary and performed by whom
4) Cervical gel, applied by whom
5) Amount of freedom of movement
6) IV
7) Pitocin
8) Intrauterine catheter
9) urinary catheters

Delivery Preferences:

1) Position, vertical, squatting, side-lying or semi-sitting
2) Mirror for viewing of baby during delivery
3) Freedom to touch baby during delivery
4) Mother-directed pushing as urge begins, or staff directed pushing as soon as the cervix is fully dilated.
5) Episiotomy desires, no or ask first
6) Forceps, vacuum extraction options and desires, level of doctors expertise and willingness to perform either.
7) When a C-Section is appropriate.
8) Cutting of cord by partner
9) Delivery of placenta naturally or medically induced
9) Baby immediately placed on abdomen and breasts
10) Dim lights for newborn's eyes
11) Breastfeeding immediately
12) Private time for family bonding
13) Video camera allowed

Care of newborn:

1) rooming-in or nursery, brought to mother only for nursing, overnight?
2) newborn exams performed after bonding period
3) feeding preferences, breast only, formula only, supplemental bottles only
4) pacifier use, yes or no
5) circumcision, yes or no

As a guest at the delivery, you must try to be accommodating in all situations and not cause any confrontations while supporting your daughter's care and well being at the same time.

"My mother did everything we asked her to, both as far as preparation went and at the actual birth. She went on the hospital tour with us."
Rika, mother

Going to one of the ultrasound appointments where you can see the baby is an exciting opportunity for both of you. Usually this is performed after twelve weeks and maybe more than once if your daughter is considered high risk. The husband often attends the first ultrasound but you may be invited also; or you may be asked to come for the next one. How exciting to see your grandchild move in the womb! You may even see a family resemblance in the infant's facial outline. Many technicians will allow your daughter to make a video tape of the ultrasound or a photo, so if you cannot go she may be able to send it to you. Many grandparents today are showing off pictures of their new grandchild while he is still in the womb, long before they have baby portraits.

If you are able, go on a visit or two with your daughter to her doctor's office. While many of you live out of town and this may not be possible, try to arrange it. Getting to know the doctor, who has your daughter and grandchild's well being in his control, will help you on delivery day. The more of an understanding you have of how the doctor and your daughter and son-in-law relate, the easier it will be to blend into their threesome during delivery.

Your primary goal is to be a subtle extra helper, friend and comforter. Familiarizing yourself with the hospital and getting to know your daughter's doctor will aid everyone on delivery day.

Chapter Seven
Birth Education Classes

"If you are going to have someone in the room who has never seen a baby being born or has never had a baby, prepare them." Stephanie, mother

"There needed to be more information about what was and was not allowed to be done by the helpers.   There was a bit of a feeling of uselessness." Cathy, grandmother

"I have had five children and am expecting again. We have had grandmothers at every birth and even a grandfather, aunts, and other children.   When they are properly trained in what your expectation is, it is a wonderful family event." Melanie, mother

"I went into the delivery room with my daughter and I'll never do it again. We had gone through all the delivery classes together and I thought I was prepared, but it just does something to your heart and gut to see your precious daughter laying there in such pain and there is nothing you can do to help her. I was so concerned for my daughter and the baby that I could hardly take it. I stayed with her, because she wanted me to, but it tore my heart to pieces.   Now I know why they won't let doctors operate on family -- it's just too emotional -- you lose all sense of judgment. It's hard to watch your child in pain." Judith, grandmother

Most expectant couples take classes in birth preparation in the 6th or 7th month of pregnancy. These classes are offered by many different organizations and can be found by calling your local hospital or community education office. There is a list of contacts at the end of the book with the addresses and phone numbers for the International Childbirth Education Association, The American Academy of Husband-Coached Childbirth(Bradley Method)and APSO-Lamaze.

These classes are designed to help teach the coach (usually the husband) how to help his wife during labor and delivery and to educate the couple about the birth process. Students learn the stages of labor and what to expect as well as many helpful pain reducing and comforting measures that they can employ. They learn about diet, exercise and general health to be used during pregnancy and after. While the aim of a "prepared or natural" childbirth course is to teach patients how to reduce or eliminate pain and the need for medication during labor and delivery, the course instructor will acquaint each couple with routine hospital equipment and interventions used in case they desire or require it. As you can see, these classes offer helpful and important information beyond pain relief and drug choices, especially for first time parents.

The two popular methods of prepared (un-medicated)childbirth education today are: the Bradley Method and the Lamaze method. While the Bradley method stresses working with your body's natural processes, the Lamaze method teaches distraction techniques as a relief for discomfort. Even if a woman decides to have pain relieving drugs, these methods will help her while she is still at home and may help postpone medication until later in her labor.

An informed patient, one who knows how her body works and what she might encounter, is better able to assist in her delivery. This makes it easier for everyone. An informed coach is expected to help a laboring woman make the labor management choices when they arise and to offer comfort measures and nurturing during her travail.

Discussions with other couples in childbirth classes offer support for nervous new parents and assure them that they are not alone in their concerns. It brings together second time parents who "survived" to tell about their experience. This is sometimes good and sometimes not so good, but always of interest. Often lasting friendships are initiated at a birthing class.

Since it has probably been over twenty years since you gave birth, your hospital birth experience will be different than what couples encounter today. Even your labor and memories of your labor at home before you got to the hospital, while interesting, usually won't prepare your daughter for what will happen to her because all labors and deliveries are so different. Your daughter needs to obtain most of her birth information from her childbirth class, from recent publications, and from discussions with her doctor.

> "After four babies, I still couldn't recognize my
> own daughter's onset of labor because it was so
> different than any of my own had been. I felt as
> if I didn't know anything!" Lynn, mother

If you are allowed by the instructor to attend one or two of the childbirth preparation classes your daughter is attending with her coach, I encourage you to go. I only caution you to listen more than you talk, because things have changed so much since you gave birth. If you have never seen a baby being born because you were sedated when you gave birth, and if you plan to be in the delivery room when your grandchild is born, then attending class the night the birth movie is shown might be helpful.

Some hospitals have a class for grandparents. A nurse or administrator takes them on a tour just like that of the new moms and spends some time talking about what value they have as grandparents. The instructor will encourage you to talk about your experiences, especially if you were at the birth of a previous grandchild. Many grandparents, having never seen a birth before, are very scared and not sure they want to be there. After all, it is so intimate. They may not be as comfortable with the human body as today's society assumes. Call the hospital where your grandchild will be born and ask if they have a grandparent class. If not, why not start one, or encourage the hospital to start one?

In preparation for attending the birth of your grandchild, or trying to decide if you want to, it would be helpful to read a few books and encourage your spouse to read them also. I have included in the resource section some books you may enjoy because they are current and informative but not too graphic. There is an excellent program on The Learning Channel (cable T. V.) called "A Baby Story." This program takes you into the delivery room for many different births, two are shown every day Monday through Friday. It will give you more of an idea of what the birth might be like and what you will experience.

You do not need to know everything that your daughter will want to know, but depending on how much you have kept up with the new technology, you might want to familiarize yourself with the tools of the birthing trade today.

> "My mom attended the birth of my son. I really wanted her there to share our experience as both of her birth experiences were lonely and scary. She was very encouraging during the delivery and was the first one to notice we had a son. She read the *Birth Partner* by Penny Simkin so she was prepared. I feel that my son and his grandmother share a very special bond." Lori, mother

If your daughter has a special situation, such as a high risk pregnancy, or a scheduled C-Section, twins, or a baby with special needs, then you might want to contact a support group in advance. These groups can offer not only education but also empathy and understanding. They can help the family prepare for the burdens or hardships which may occur. I have included a list of some of these organizations in the resource section as well.

The important thing about preparing yourself for the upcoming life changing event is not how much you know but how to create the best atmosphere possible so that this event can be fondly remembered by everyone.

Chapter Eight
Birth - A Three Act Production

I shall describe in this chapter a hospital LDR birth because that is the most popular birth today. However, more and more births are taking place at home and at birthing centers, depending on the region in which a couple may live, what their wishes are, and what their budget can afford. As mentioned earlier, birthing center and home births are very different from hospital births, and have almost no intervention, so you wouldn't need as much information for attending that type of birth. Another reason I describe an LDR hospital birth is because sometimes, no matter what the original plan, a hospital birth becomes necessary. In that case, it helps to be familiar with the equipment and procedures used in most of today's hospital births so you won't be frightened or intimidated.

When your daughter is admitted she will probably already be dilated from three to five centimeters and will be in early labor with her contractions about five minutes apart. If you are not with her already, you should be on your way to the hospital.

She will be given a routine examination and her blood pressure, temperature, pulse and respiration will be checked. Some hospitals have what they call a "triage" where she will be checked first and then transferred to labor and delivery when active labor is evident.

Her doctor will be called by the hospital staff and informed of her condition. The staff, acting on his instructions for labor management, and having read her birth plan, will begin ordered procedures. The first procedures will probably be monitoring with an external fetal heart monitor as soon the laboring woman has dressed in a gown and settled into bed.

Sometimes an IV of glucose will be started. (Many hospitals believe having an IV already inserted saves time if drugs need to be administered quickly during labor.) She may be allowed to walk around, dragging the IV pole with her, if she has no other complications. However, she will be asked to return to bed periodically so the staff can check the baby's heart rate by re-attaching the external monitor. While these minimal hospital procedures are very common even something as simple as an IV can prevent a woman from doing what makes her comfortable, like taking a whirlpool bath or shower. (The simple act of taking a shower can offer immense relief from the discomfort of labor.)So while husbands are told to bring their swimming trunks so they can assist their wife as she labors in the shower, most will never get the opportunity. Like other things, the birth experience that is often described during the hospital tour is not the birth experience most women actually have.

Additional comfort measures (besides walking or bathing) which may be utilized now include the application of heating pads, the use of gentle massage, and the performing of relaxation and breathing exercises. If she has freedom of movement, a delivering woman will find out quickly what position feels best for her. My daughter-in-law, Debbie, spent most of her labor sitting on the toilet, while others have squatted, used a special birthing stool, or spent most of their time on their hands and knees on the floor. (This last position, by the way, relieves back pain by taking the baby's weight off the spine.)

Acupressure, a form of pressure relief originally developed in the Orient, may bring relief and promote progress in labor without the use of drugs. It certainly can't hurt to try. Press a finger or thumb on the back of the patient's hand where the bones of the thumb and index fingers join, applying pressure to the index finger side for ten to fifteen seconds: repeat three times. Rest between applications and repeat as many times as desired by the birthing mother. Another pressure point you can try is at the base of the leg, on the inner side about five inches above and slightly behind the ankle bone.

If your daughter experiences extreme low back pain, then counter pressure with your fist or a firm object like a tennis ball, rolling pin or soda can will offer the best relief. The patient will tell you where and how hard to press, usually very hard. Another method of relief for back pain is the pelvic rock or getting up on hands and knees so the baby's weight is off your back. Obviously, you can only use this method if you are free to move about the bed. A heating pad also works wonders. Take one of the instant heat packs which are available in all drug stores with you so you will not have to wait for the staff to get one. (It took us over an hour to get one for my daughter after numerous requests at one hospital.) Back labor pain is the most difficult to experience but can be one of the easiest pains to relieve if you have freedom of movement. While this pain relief function is usually performed by the husband/coach, you may be called upon to help out occasionally.

If allowed, the birthing woman may find relief and distraction by sucking on a lollipop. In a recent study done at Baylor University Medical Center in Dallas, doctors found that sucking on a lollipop before surgery reduced anxiety significantly while having no effects on gastric juices that could interfere with anesthesia for surgery. So if applied to a woman in labor, a sucker is a safe, fun, tasty relaxation method to use. Some hospitals will allow a laboring woman to drink a soda and eat ice, but if you are in a hospital that won't allow lollipops, ice or soda, you may be able to have the attending physician give his permission. The chances of a woman needing general anesthetic for childbirth (which is why hospitals want the patient's stomach empty) are slim in the 90's. If a laboring woman has an upset stomach she will refuse food or drink. Sometimes just a wet washcloth to suck or bite is relief enough. Some women ask for chap stick to moisten their lips.

Most patients today are required to wear an external monitor when not walking around. The external monitor consists of two straps which are placed around the mother's abdomen and are attached to the portable Electronic Fetal Monitor Machine located on a nearby table. One strap detects the fetal heart rate and the other indicates the mother's contractions. If the mother wishes to walk around, she has only to undo the belts at the Velcro closings and leave them on the bed. They can be reattached quickly when she returns to bed. External monitoring is easily interrupted by a patient's movements in bed and often the straps need to be repositioned frequently during labor. While this is a bothersome task, the external fetal monitor is less invasive than the internal monitor because it does not require internal insertion.

A nurse might suggest that the laboring woman try nipple stimulation if labor is slow. By gently rolling her nipple between her thumb and forefinger or gently caressing her nipple with her hand in a back and forth motion, she may bring on a contraction. The stimulation causes the release of her own natural form of pitocin called oxytocin which in turn causes the contraction. Repeating the stimulation after each contraction for about twenty minutes or until the next contraction starts should help produce regular contractions. It doesn't always work, even if the cervix is ripe, but it is worth trying before resorting to drugs to augment labor.

Prostaglandin gel is often applied internally on the cervix to soften it. It may be done by a resident as soon as the laboring woman is settled in her hospital room or it may have been done the day before by her doctor if delivery was overdue and an induction of labor prescribed. This procedure, designed to help Mother Nature, is not too uncomfortable or invasive, is very safe and works well on most patients. Induction is nearly always successful since the introduction of prostaglandin gel to help ripen the cervix. This procedure is without complications although the ripening of the cervix (first stage of labor) may take a couple of days.

If labor is augmented with Pitocin, to speed things up, it will be administered through an IV line with an infusion pump. (If one is not already in place, it will be inserted now.) Pitocin was developed in the 1950's by a biochemist and it won him a Nobel Prize. It is an exact copy of oxytocin, the hormone produced by the pituitary gland of pregnant women to cause the uterus to contract. Pitocin contractions usually bring an increased level of pain. The doctors will disagree with this, but ask any mother who has had "pit" and has also delivered without it and they will tell you they experienced a noticeable difference. These procedures, the Pitocin and cervix gel, usually require close monitoring of the patient after they have been initiated and will further restrict her movement, usually requiring her to remain in bed hooked up to the external monitor.

Nearly all women who deliver in hospitals now get Pitocin. Most labors are not "perfect" so doctors routinely prescribe pitocin to "help them".

The doctor, if he is not already on call at the hospital, will hopefully arrive to assist in the late part of labor and for delivery. Prior to his arrival most of the care is directed through phone calls by the attending nurse and resident on call.

The "bag of water", amniotic sac, may be broken by the doctor if the cervix is dilated enough for him to perform the procedure (called amniotomy). This procedure is usually done to speed up labor, but is not necessary in most normal labors. Here again, most all women delivering in a hospital setting today will have their bag of water broken early in labor to "speed things up". But this procedure increases the likelihood that augmented pain relief will be needed, since the contractions will feel more intense, especially if pitocin is also being administered. After the bag of water is broken, the physician may want to attach an internal fetal monitor to the baby's scalp for closer monitoring. This is done by inserting a wire into the vagina and cervix to reach the infants head. This wire will remain (and can be felt) between the woman's legs as the baby moves. While more reliable than the external monitor, the internal monitor further limits a woman's ability to move around. It must be disconnected from the monitor unit if she wishes to go to the bathroom and she will not be allowed to walk around at her leisure. While neither procedure is painful (to the mother), both are invasive. Luckily, they are usually performed before the laboring woman is in the midst of uncomfortable contractions.

If artificial rupture of the membranes is done to speed up labor, an intrauterine pressure catheter may be inserted internally, through the vagina, also. It gives the staff an estimation of the force of each contraction.

High blood pressure can cause seizures and possible danger to the infant as well if left untreated. So if the patient's blood pressure is elevated, as it often is during late pregnancy, an automatic blood pressure cuff will be attached and remain in place throughout labor, taking periodic readings automatically. While this equipment can be disconnected or removed, or taken with her as in the case of the IV, so the patient can go to the bathroom on her own, the staff usually is reluctant to allow her to do so. Most patients with high blood pressure are confined to bed on their left side (blood pressure is lower when a patient is on her left side). One noted gynecologist even wrote that reclining on the left side is the position most advantageous to promote dilation. I know of many patients who would disagree with that and emphasize that this position is not the most *comfortable* even if it produces results. I personally cannot believe that working against gravity could be advantageous. This theory says that the women who for centuries squatted to deliver their young were doing it wrong. Rather, I believe lying in bed to labor has been promoted by hospitals and physicians and is not natural or advantageous at all. In any event, the combination of equipment utilized at this point may require the installation of a urinary catheter or at the very least require that a bed pan be provided. The hospital staff is not going to want to disconnect everything or let your daughter transport it across the room to go to the bathroom.

As labor progresses to the active phase and increasing discomfort is felt, further pain relief may be requested. At this point your daughter's labor will have dilated her cervix anywhere from 6-8cm. She may be moved to the "good room" if she has been in a labor room up until now. If an IV has not been started yet, it will have to be started before an epidural is administered. The epidural procedure, the most commonly used medication for pain relief during childbirth today, can take up to 45 minutes and will be uncomfortable for both your daughter and probably you too. It requires the anesthesiologist to insert a catheter in the lower back of the patient. It is often difficult to insert and unfortunately is done during a very uncomfortable stage of labor. You may wish to get a cup of coffee at this time. After the epidural is in place, both of you will feel better for awhile.

At this point your daughter will be confined to bed completely because she will experience numbness in the lower half of her body. She will be relieved of pain and discomfort almost entirely and may even take a nap for a few minutes if it is quiet. She should reposition herself occasionally so the epidural is not pooling in one side of her body causing pain to surface on the other side. Because the sensation of a full bladder will be impaired, a urinary catheter now is mandatory and must be inserted (if not already done) unless birth is imminent. Laboring women must empty their bladder about every hour. The bladder lies near the cervix and a full bladder can prevent labor from progressing as it should and be dangerous if left full in the event a C-Section become necessary.

When my daughter Christine was sent to the operating room for a C-Section her catheter had apparently not been inserted properly and her bladder was full. After the incision, when the bladder "popped out," the doctor had to drain it with a syringe. If he had nicked the bladder it would have been a very serious complication. While we, as guests at he birth, should not have to know everything and check on the staff as they are doing their job, we should keep in mind that they do sometimes make mistakes. Some knowledge on your part, being aware of what is going on, is good advise for any family member visiting any hospitalized loved one.

If the procedures outlined have been instituted, your daughter is completely under the management of equipment and the hospital staff, usually flat on her back, or semi-reclining and confined to bed. While seeing your daughter hooked up to six or seven apparatuses may be frightening, many women are going through this experience every day and don't seem to mind. If you are picturing your daughter now with a permanent blood pressure cuff hissing on one arm, an internal fetal monitor wire, intrauterine pressure catheter and bladder catheter between her legs, an IV drip and Pitocin line in her other arm, and a epidural line in her back, let me assure you that it looks worse than it is. This is the picture of a normal laboring woman in most major hospitals today; a science-assisted birth. This was not the picture

I had in my mind when I went to the delivery of my first grandchild. That's probably why I was so upset.

Although patients are assured of pain free labor with an epidural by their childbirth instructor or doctor, it's not quite true. There is pain in early labor before an epidural can be given and before the actual delivery during the pushing stage when the dose of epidural is lowered so the patient can feel the contractions and assist in the delivery. There is as yet no such thing as painless childbirth. While pain and discomfort may be minimal they are still part of having a baby with or without an epidural. I think laboring women today would have easier labors if they stoically accepted this truth instead of believing that having a baby was similar to having a tooth filled. Having a baby is not "the worst pain you will ever have" as my mother told me, but it is uncomfortable and hurts. Even a planned C-Section causes pain but the pain is after the delivery. So while women might be expecting a painless childbirth, technology is not there yet. Give the doctors a few more years to work on our bodies and design new equipment and it may not be far off.

Although I think the pain and discomfort of childbirth is preferable to the pain and discomfort and restriction of all these needles and equipment, not everyone agrees. We all experience pain differently and can tolerate different levels. In addition, all labors have different pain patterns. Your daughter knows that pain relief is available with minimal risk to her and her baby, and she is aware of the monitoring, intervention and immobility which comes with her choices. If this is her plan for her delivery, then all you can do is support her.

As I mentioned before, she may look like she is in intensive care but she isn't in danger, so you should relax. Have a lollipop yourself. Being familiar with these procedures may offer you some peace of mind and relieve your anxiety. One hopes you will not be frightened when you see your daughter like this for the first time, as I was.

> "My son-in-law was a bit concerned that I would
> get in the way but he ended up very relieved that
> I was there. I let him be 'in charge' and asked

> what I could do for him. I saw a different side
> of him which I admired. He was scared but did
> anything he could to help my daughter." Denese,
> grandmother

The next stage is transition and it signals the end of labor and the beginning of birth. You will know when transition has arrived because there will be a period when nothing seems to relieve the pain anymore. At this stage the cervix is almost completely dilated. Your daughter may say "I give up, I can't do it, the epidural isn't working." She may scream at her husband or anyone in the room including you. She might vomit, tremble, have hot or cold flashes or all of the above. Don't be surprised and don't be hurt if she yells at you; she doesn't mean it. If the nurse is not in the room, now is the time to get her/him. This crankiness and chaos is a sure sign the baby is almost here.

> "My mother and mother-in-law were both in the
> room as I labored but they left for the delivery.
> Good thing too; if my mother stroked my hair
> one more time before I had that epidural I think I
> would have yanked myself bald!" Amber,
> mother

Now the pushing stage of labor begins. This second stage of labor will expel the baby. The delivery room will get very busy now and you may feel left out. Get the camera ready and take up a position slightly out of the way. It may take several hours for a first time mother or only several pushes for an experienced laborer. If birth isn't imminent you may be invited to help the coach lift your daughter up as she pushes or hold her legs. During this phase the baby is pushed down through the birth canal. The "crowning" is when the baby's head can be seen. You will probably be asked if you want to look; everyone else will be looking, so why not? I do suggest however, that you do not capture it on film. This is one moment best left to memory, not film. Sometimes the baby will crown and then slip back up the birth canal. In cases like this, the use of forceps or suction extraction may be necessary to help ease the baby out. If this stage of labor has been lengthy and the doctor does not wish to use forceps or suction, a C-Section may be suggested. The actual birth of the baby ends this stage of labor.

Your son or son-in-law may be allowed to help cut the cord as the doctor directs him. This is a good photo opportunity and the doctor may ask if you are ready to take the picture. The newborn is then placed on the mother's abdomen. The third stage of labor is the delivery of the placenta or afterbirth. It causes minimal discomfort and most of the non-medical guests in the room will prefer to ignore it. The delivery of the placenta is the bloodiest part of the birth, and while it is important the doctor examines the placenta to be sure it appears normal, no one else in the room will probably want to see it. They will be too busy with the new baby.

In her delight with her new infant, she may not even notice the expulsion of the placenta (the final stage of childbirth) or the stitches the doctor may need to insert to repair any tearing or to stitch an episiotomy closed if one was performed. (An episiotomy is a surgical incision made to enlarge the vaginal opening to prevent tearing. While episiotomies have been performed since 1945 most physicians will try to avoid their use since only about 30% of births produce vaginal tearing. A forceps delivery will require an episiotomy.) Sometimes an IV of pitocin is administered after the expulsion of the placenta to aid in the shrinking of the uterus, especially in a woman who is not breastfeeding.

Newborn babies are not always attractive. While the movies try to make them appear more true to life now by smearing them with cottage cheese and strawberry jam, the real thing may cause you to hold your breath and your praise for a moment. Heads are often temporally misshapen during their passage down the birth canal and some babies are still covered with vernix, a white cheesy material which protected the baby's skin. Despite some blood and an excess amount of hair, I am sure this infant will be the most beautiful one you have ever seen in a few minutes after he is cleaned up. Try not to blurt out as I did "what an ugly baby" when you first see your new grandchild. It won't get you invited back. (I was forgiven and invited back.)

After a short rest on the mother's abdomen, the baby is taken to be weighed, measured, and cleaned. Footprints are taken and an ID bracelet is put on the baby, with a matching one for the new father and mother. Eye drops, as mandated by law, are put in the baby's eyes to prevent infection. An injection of vitamin K is also given to help the baby's blood to clot. The infant is then returned to the mother who is now feeling "no pain" and smiling profusely. The staff will leave the family alone to spend some quiet time together. If you were not in the room for the birth, you will be invited in now. Usually, the family will be allowed two hours to visit before the baby is taken to the nursery for observation and your daughter will be moved to her permanent room if she is staying overnight. It would be good for you to leave the new parents alone with their infant for a few minutes during this time so they can bond, and besides, you need to call the rest of the family.

> "Everyone present at a birth must be focused on the mother and child. Anyone who cannot subserviate themselves totally to the process of bringing new life into the world should not be at a birth, at home or in a hospital." Nadia, mother

Stages of childbirth(labor):

FIRST Stage (Act I):   When the cervix (opening of the uterus) dilates or opens to ten centimeters (cm).

Early or latent phase -- Beginning, irregular contractions which are manageable dilate the cervix from one to five centimeters with effacement (thinning) of the cervix going from zero to ninety percent. This stage could last from a few hours to a couple of days.

A*ctive* phase -- Regular contractions dilate the cervix to about four to eight centimeters, averaging about one centimeter per hour. Contractions are harder and longer in duration, with the cervix one hundred percent effaced. This stage could last three to four hours. Baby's station(position in the birth canal) is about minus four to zero.

Transition phase -- contractions about every two minutes, which dilate the cervix from eight or nine centimeters to ten while the baby is pushed down the birth canal. This stage could last anywhere from fifteen minutes to one or two hours. Baby's station is now zero to plus two. During this stage the baby's head turns sideways in preparation for birth.

SECOND Stage (Act II):   The delivery of the baby. This stage may take from as little as a few minutes to three hours. It is time to push. Dilation and effacement are obviously complete and the station is plus two to plus four, the baby's head is crowning.

THIRD Stage (Act III):   Delivery of the placenta, with one or two final contractions, can last from five to thirty minutes.
(End of Act III)

As a note, obstetricians estimate the average labor for a first baby lasts about twelve hours after active labor begins (from three to five centimeters dilation); however, a recent study by the University of New Mexico indicated that from four centimeters dilation to birth the average new mother spent 19.4 hours in labor.

During her first delivery, my daughter-in-law spent ten and one half hours dilating from two centimeters to delivery with no pitocin or pain relief. She was aided with delivery only by forceps.

My daughter, however, was subjected to a C-section, due to "failure to progress", (and because her doctor didn't *do* forceps or suction extraction delivery assistance procedures) after only about ten hours of labor during the birth of her first baby.

It might be necessary for medical institutions to stop rushing women and readjust the arbitrary clock they use before forcing a woman to "have this baby now", especially when the baby appears to be in no distress. This timing is based on a Friedman curve which was derived from statistical norms. According to this chart, women are supposed to dilate one and one half centimeters every hour or after they have reached four centimeters they should dilate about one centimeter an hour.

This timing is part of the hospital's protocol and is often tied to the induction of pain relief or other procedures such as the breaking of the bag of water. Encourage your daughter to find out the hospital's protocol during her hospital tour and suggest that she ask her doctor if he uses forceps or suction as part of his delivery procedures. In the event that he does not, she can ask him if she will be allowed to request another doctor to assist in the delivery who is experienced in forceps or suction deliveries. Many of the newer doctors are not experienced with forceps deliveries and would prefer to do a C-Section.

In my daughter's case, her husband could have asked for another doctor's opinion about whether a C-Section was necessary or refuse the C-Section or ask for another doctor to take over her care who was experienced with forceps deliveries, thereby avoiding an unnecessary C-Section, since she and the baby were never in distress. While being prepared for transfer to the OR, Christine actually had the urge to push, the baby was now ready to be born, but she was told not to push--it was too late. She had passed the time allotted in their protocol to deliver her baby and they were now in the C-Section mode wheeling her to the OR. A C-Section is major surgery and should be reserved for emergencies such as fetal distress or in cases where the baby is too large or in the wrong position when vaginal delivery would be hazardous to the infant.

Birth, while designed by nature, is now managed by technology and physicians; both of which are, even at their best, imperfect creations. The patient and her husband need to be educated and responsible for their own care and not relinquish control to others unless it's an emergency.

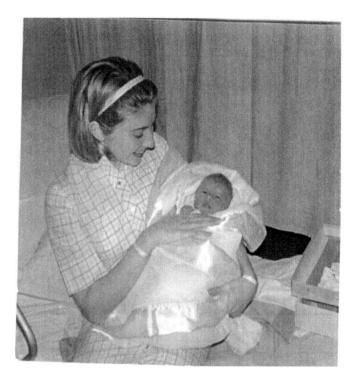

Leaving the hospital with my daughter, Christine, in 1968.

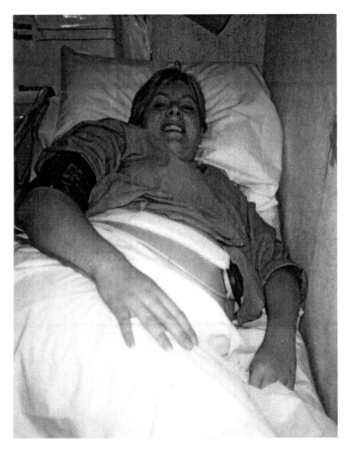

My daughter, Christine being checked in triage during her first pregnancy in 1993.

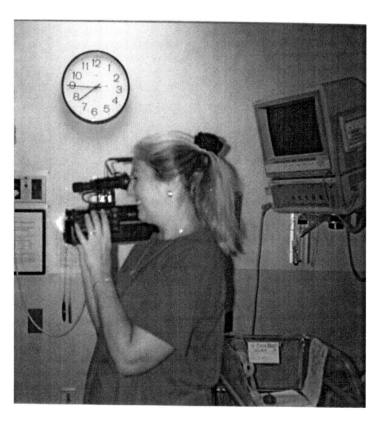

Taking video pictures at Erik's birth, 1993.

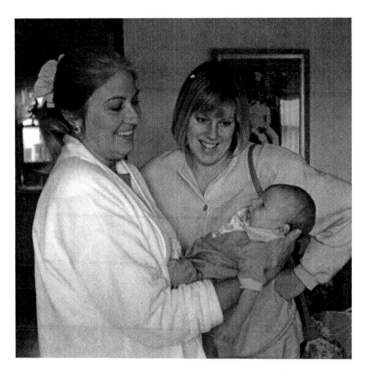

Christine and I with my first grandson, Leif Erik, 1993.

Christine being comforted by a visit from Erik during the induction of her stillborn baby, Joseph, in 1995.

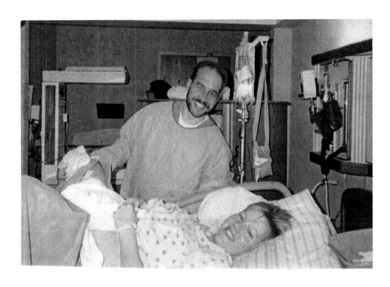

Christine and Dr. Bork during the birth of my third grandson, Thomas, in 1996.

Christine in labor with her fourth boy, Andrew, in 1998.

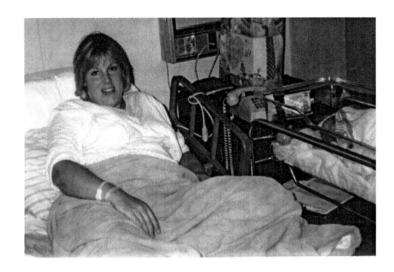

Christine with Andrew after his birth.

Chapter Nine
What Is Your Role?

Are you still wondering what you will be doing? You may feel that you will just be in the way or you may think that you will be too uncomfortable to be in the room during delivery.

If you have something to do, a plan for yourself, then I think the birth event will not only be pleasant, but will be memorable. We all need to feel needed and you are very definitely needed. You have a unique place at the birth which no one else can fill as well as you can.

> "I have to say, my mom wasn't much help and just couldn't make me happy, but I am so glad she was there. Moms are wonderful and we've all wanted our moms when we were in pain."
> Deb, mother

> "I concentrated on just being there when they needed me and being sure I wasn't in the way."
> Denese, grandmother

Photographer

Many grandparents, both grandmothers and grandfathers, are very comfortable being the family historian by taking pictures. If this has been a role you enjoy then by all means consider this as one of your necessary functions at the birth. It is sometimes more comfortable to be behind a camera where no one can see you. Taking photographs is a job which a new father may be glad to give up so he can spend all his time with his wife and baby. If he has to take all the pictures then he isn't in them; he misses out on much of the birth. You also will be more likely to take "G" rated pictures. Sometimes the expectant father is so excited he takes pictures that his wife won't let anyone see. They are obviously more comfortable with each others' naked bodies than you and the rest of the family, so what seems appropriate to them in the emotional arena of childbirth may not be appropriate when viewed by the rest of the family at Sunday dinner.

Whether taking video pictures or snapshots, you should practice! Get all the equipment ready ahead of time and make sure you know how to use it, have extra batteries, etc. The doctor will usually wait for a second, like when the cord is cut, for you to take a picture, but he can't wait for you to change film. If you have a tripod for the camera, set it up in advance at an appropriate angle (out of the way of the staff) and enjoy the birth too.

Another suggestion for you if you are not filming the birth is to take a tape recorder to record the first cry of your grandchild. Some have recorded the entire labor, but there is often a lot of screaming or swearing going on which your daughter may not want saved for posterity--she would rather forget. Even if your daughter says she doesn't want pictures because she looks awful, this is one of life's greatest events and your daughter will be glad to have pictures later. A snapshot doesn't have to be shown to others if she objects. I put a picture in each of my children's baby book, showing me leaving the hospital with them. When they got married, I gave them their baby books and they enjoyed seeing all the pictures. No matter how bad or fat I looked then, to them I looked young and happy. I was.

> "My husband felt removed from the birth experience because he was videotaping and my mother did what he felt he should be doing." Rika, mother

> "My son-in-law wanted to videotape and therefore my presence was helpful, because I was able to be with my daughter." Ingrid, grandmother

"I took the video pictures so my son-in-law could be with my daughter and be *in* the pictures. They both appreciated that and it forced me to give them a little space to themselves." Lynn, grandmother

Baby sitter

Maybe you might feel more comfortable being a baby-sitter for other children in the family who are invited to the birth, especially if the birth is to take place in a birthing center. This is a natural role for a grandparent and if you are comfortable with it, then that's what you should do. Even if you are not in the actual room for the birth, you and the other children will be invited in immediately afterward to see the newborn. The old days when no children were allowed to visit in the hospital are gone, thank goodness. This would be a good time to read a book about a child whose mom is having a baby. There are many available in bookstores and libraries. *The New Baby* by Fred Rogers and Jim Judkis and *The Berenstein Bears' New Baby* by Stan Berenstein are two. Be sure the one you purchase is age appropriate for your grandchild.

Guest Monitor

During labor most women lose their sense of privacy; they may throw off their clothes entirely and not care who is there. You will be able to help monitor the visitors and make sure they are welcome in the birthing area. You may be the only guard at the door to filter guests in accordance with your daughter's wishes thereby assuring her of privacy and quiet when she wants it. You will know if she is in the shower or having a pelvic exam and can ask visitors to wait in the lounge. Remember, her husband will be busy trying to nurture her and see to her other needs.

> "One thing that has an impact on my feelings about people being at the birth is the fact that I am German. I am a lot more relaxed about nudity than most Americans. I was completely naked during the birth and have everything on videotape." Rika, mother

Relief Coach

You can be the relief coach when your son or son-in-law needs a break, as he will from time to time, if only to eat! He will be hungry even if his wife isn't. While he is gone, you may be asked to do something your daughter didn't want to ask him to do. It may be a special massage you used when she was a child. She may enjoy having you comb her hair or do some other comforting or cleaning measures. Maybe a sponge bath or a clean gown would make her happy. No matter how much husbands love their wives, they are still men and sometimes they just don't get it. Often it takes another woman to understand what will make another woman feel better or what level of hygiene will aid her comfort and relaxation and help her feel good about herself. Perhaps the room has been too noisy or the lights too bright and some quiet reassuring talk and a nap is needed. During football season the T. V. is usually tuned to a game. Dim the lights and turn off the T. V. for awhile.

> "When I soiled myself in labor, I was more comfortable with my mother cleaning me up than my husband. I mean, she had done that so many times before (granted, I was slightly smaller then.)" Rika, mother

Pain Management

This would be a good time to use touch therapy. A couple of the most sensitive areas are the fingertips and soles of the feet. You could suggest a foot rub. Or, just lightly stroke her hand. I have found that to be very comforting and very loving. Remember, your touch, your skin is softer than her husbands. Be sure the back rub or massage is desired by your daughter before you begin and stop when she asks without feeling hurt or offended. Like a wounded animal, her personality may change as the level of pain rises.

Throughout this book I use the word pain often, however, I never personally thought childbirth was painful. I drove myself to the hospital with my second child, Christine, and she was born an hour later. I hadn't felt any labor contractions. I had a natural delivery without any medication for my third child, Jolie, and never felt pain - merely - discomfort on the ride to the hospital. While I seem to have been spared "painful" labors, I realize most women haven't. I do not want readers of this book to think that childbirth is pain free. So I use the word *pain* in most cases, rather than trying to elude the reader by using only the word *discomfort* as many texts and childbirth educators do.

> "My mother was wonderful doing everything I asked her to do and not getting upset when I yelled at her for holding my hand the "wrong" way. (That wrong way only exists when you're in labor, I think.)." Rika, mother

Errands

You can be the "go-for"; securing food, drinks, hot pads and ice, accepting flowers if they arrive, making phone calls which are needed for last minute dog care or child care. You can help your daughter in the bathroom as she struggles with an IV, an open gown and a extended painful stomach. You can help her brush her teeth after several hours of labor which may have included vomiting and maybe get her make-up bag for her after delivery if she feels like freshening up before receiving company. Ask your daughter what you can do for her. Avoid the tendency to take over or "mother too much." She will probably tell you if you do. Again, don't be overly sensitive. Her hormones and feelings may be running amok!

> "I worried that she'd smother me with worry and hover over me. I worried that she and my husband would disagree about something. I worried needlessly about a million things." Sheila, mother

> "I felt a lot of sympathy for my daughter, I felt helpless not being able to do more, and the birth was the reward for our patience. I tried to stay out of the way, tried to be quiet, but I felt that I was helpful." Ingrid, grandmother

Support

You will be around to help make decisions if her husband needs help. You need to support your son-in-law if he has a difficult decision to make. Obviously this is easier if he consults you before he makes the decision, but if he doesn't, you must try to understand that he is doing the best he can. One of the most difficult aspects of being present is knowing that your daughter's medical care is entirely in the hands of her husband. You are no longer responsible for her in the eyes of the law or by the hospital staff. It will be hard to see your daughter in pain and not be able to make it go away. It will be hard to be silent if her husband makes a medical decision on her behalf with which you disagree, but you must gently give suggestions and get along with everyone. If you don't, they will ask you to leave. You have to believe that the hospital staff or midwife is doing what needs to be done and that they all have your daughter's best interests in mind. If you have met your daughter's doctor beforehand, you should be able to trust him with the suggestions he makes. If you have established a good relationship with the nurses, they will usually support you. During the birth of my stillborn grandson, Joseph, there was a last minute change and the delivery was moved to a surgical room instead of the LDR. I was told I could not stay for the birth. The attending nurse, who had seen that I was helpful in comforting my daughter and unfazed by blood and the birth process, stood up for me; I was allowed in. I will forever be in her debt. Not only did my daughter need me, I was able to recount the events to her later. She was so drugged at the time she didn't remember much. Her husband's concentration was totally on her to the exclusion of much that was happening in the room. The first moments I shared with my grandson, helping to weigh and measure him, left a memory that will forever be in my heart, even while he is gone.

In contrast, during my daughter's first delivery, the nurse asked me to leave midway through labor and although my daughter requested my presence several times, the nurse never came to get me. The next time I saw my daughter, she was being wheeled out for a C-Section. If you are in the waiting room and think you have been forgotten to be invited back, ask to speak to your daughter or her husband.

> "In some ways, I was almost overwhelmed. It hurt me to see her in pain and I had to leave the room a few times just to get control - go for several walks to keep from getting emotional."
> Denese, grandmother

> "My son-in-law was glad I was present. I think he felt my being there helped to relax my daughter, and therefore him." Phyllis, grandmother

Be Knowledgeable

The best thing you can do to make this coordination of care work smoothly is to have done some reading and self-preparation by knowing the language the doctor, midwife and your daughter and son-in-law are speaking. The middle of labor is not the time for them to explain everything to you. You and your daughter should have talked; if she shared her birth plan with you, you know her desires. If you went on the hospital tour, you know your way around and you know the hospital protocol.

Record Keeper

You can help the labor coach "time" contractions using the large clock with a second hand which is in every room. You time a contraction from the beginning of one contraction to the beginning of the next. Your daughter's contractions should be about five minutes apart when she arrives at the hospital and lasting one minute each. So if you start timing one at 10:10 p.m. upon her signal then the next one would start at 10:15 p.m. She would have a rest between 10:11 p.m.(after the contraction ended) and 10:15 p.m.(when the next contraction begins).

The following cervix chart is a helpful visual aid for you and your daughter. It will allow you to visualize how the contractions are working to open the cervix for the birth. This exercise provides encouragement and helps the time pass.

Sketch of DILATING CERVIX

Make a copy of this page and darken in each circle as labor progresses to show the progress of dilation of the cervix. If you wish, jot the time down after each stage is confirmed. This can serve as a record of the time in labor. Include it in the baby book or scrapbook.

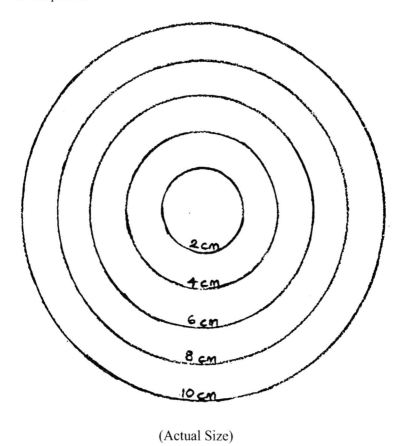

(Actual Size)

Whatever role you assume, make it a supporting one. You cannot be the star today because there already is one and it is your daughter. The co-star is her husband/coach. Defer to him rather than compete with him. During delivery stay back and give him the front row seat. By necessity, if you are taking pictures, you will have to step back in order to focus. Assume he is doing it right and don't try to show him how. I know it sounds easy now, but in the excitement you may forget. When your son leaves the room for a break, by all means sit close to your daughter until he returns, whereupon you should relinquish your seat. There are plenty of things for you to do that he may not be really excited about doing, so just remind him you are there to help, and encourage him to ask.

> "I had both my boyfriend and my mother at the birth of my child. It was great. My mother was able to give both myself and my boyfriend practical and emotional support. When my boyfriend had to take a break, my mother took over for him." Jayne, mother

One word of caution: don't be a burden to your daughter. You need to be fed, rested, and in good spirits, and you must come prepared with personal necessities such as your own medications, eye glasses, and so forth. She should not have to take care of you or see to your needs on this, one of the most important days of her life. In fact, she may be unable to do so.

If you choose not to attend the birth you can help watch other grandchildren. In the waiting room you can watch for other family members and keep them up to date. You can make phone calls that are needed. You can make sure your son-in-law or son gets food to eat by bringing it to him or relieving him in the delivery area for awhile.(Remind him to watch what he eats so his breath is fresh when he leans up close to his wife during labor. Bad breath can make a laboring woman nauseous.)

And again, you can help your son-in-law make decisions if an emergency arises. If there is a crisis, he may be unable to figure out what to do immediately and you will be a great help by providing an attentive ear as he considers the possibilities.

Regardless of whether you are in the room during the actual moment of birth, or down the hall, your caring enough to be at the hospital trying to help, and being there to see your grandchild immediately after his birth, will be the first brick in the foundation of grandparenthood.

Chapter Ten
Opening Night Is Also Dress Rehearsal

The title explains it all. The problem with birth is that there isn't a dress rehearsal. So you not only don't get a chance to practice, you don't even know what the script will be. What are your lines and when do you enter? How does the final act read? When does the curtain fall?

During the months while you wait for the birth, educating yourself along the way, you will play out many of the imagined scenes in your head and in your dreams, as will your daughter. You will see yourself navigating through each dramatic act as it unfolds and imagine your role in each scene. This is a good way to "rehearse," and the only way you can practice.

One thing you can be sure of is that you can't be sure of anything. Your daughter's labor will not be anything like yours and maybe not like any of the numerous birth stories you and she have heard since she announced her pregnancy. No matter how prepared you are something will come up for which you are not prepared. Unexpected events will force you to re-define your role and to rewrite the birth story you imagined.

> "My 5ft. 4 in. height was not tall enough to have the best view; another 12 or so inches would have been greatly appreciated.. .take a box to stand on." Pat, grandmother

So having said all that, what can you do? Hopefully this book will help you prepare for most occurrences. You read, ask questions, take a hospital tour, and attend a grandparents class if there is one.

In addition, foster a good relationship with the doctor, your son-in-law or whomever is going to be the coach, and the rest of the hospital staff, if you can. They will have to prepare you "on the spot" for anything out of the ordinary that happens.

Bring this book with you to the birth. Since the birth you expect is already in your imagination, you may have skimmed over parts of the book that you didn't think would apply to you and your daughter or daughter-in-law. If an unusual event occurs you can refresh your memory or have ready access to resources to obtain more information.

> "Because I was separated from my husband when my son was born, my mother stayed with me for the entire fifteen hours with my father in the waiting room, popping in and out all day."
> Denyse, mother

With this book in hand and armed with knowledge and good intentions, opening night should have no terror regardless of the script which is thrown at you as the curtain goes up.

Chapter Eleven
Dealing With Unexpected Events

In Chapter Eight, I tried to give you an example of a fairly typical birth as it might unfold in most major hospitals today. Some events might change that scenario.

What if your daughter is out of town when she goes into labor? What if her bag of water breaks during church a week before her due date? What if she is sick with the flu when she goes into labor and is vomiting throughout the whole event? (This actually happened to a girlfriend of mine.) What if the baby's umbilical cord is discovered by ultrasound to be wrapped around his neck and a C-section is ordered immediately? A power failure or a cab strike may occur. The hospital may be full and an LDR may not be available.

Although authorities disagree and studies contradict each other, most nurses still insist that more women go into labor during a full moon or during the extreme barometric pressure changes that surround a storm. Does low barometric pressure put unusual pressure on the amniotic fluid inducing labor in some way and does a full moon's stronger gravitational pull affect the body? These old wives tales may be proven in the future as more research is done and the process of how and when the body goes into labor is more clearly understood.

I am sure you have already thought of some additional things to worry about which I haven't mentioned; you are a parent, after all, and thereby have the monopoly on imagining the worst scenarios for any event in which your child is involved. A recent survey of older Americans indicated that over sixty percent of the adults questioned worried as much or more about their children as they did when they were teenagers. So you are not alone in your worry.

Here are some of the calamities which might occur and some suggestions for dealing with them.

First of all, remember nearly all births take longer than anyone expects, so if you are delayed by the weather, plane schedules or local labor strikes you may not miss the birth at all. Just have your daughter call you when she first thinks "this is it." Ask her not to wait until she is sure. Tell her that you would rather make an extra trip to the hospital or arrive in town early than miss everything. A first time mother may be in active labor as long as twelve hours. Of course, if you are able to stay at her house around the last week before her due date (week 38-39), then your chances of missing the birth diminish. Only four percent of babies are born on their due date: My first child, John, was one of them. Most babies, about eighty-five percent, are born between weeks 37 and 42 (within two weeks before and after the due date) and ninety-six percent arrive within a week of their due date, either before or after. Three percent of all pregnancies last over 42 weeks and only eleven to twelve percent of deliveries occur before 37 weeks. Most doctors today will not let a pregnant woman go more than two weeks past her due date(42 weeks) because of the risk of stillbirth or other major complications. If you are coming from out of town and this is a first baby, arriving during the week the baby is due is usually safe. Some hospitals offer rental beepers for expectant fathers to carry during the important final weeks. You may be able to rent one as well.

If your daughter has a good sense of humor, small inconveniences like the flu or foul weather need not destroy her overall experience, but you need to maintain a calm demeanor for the birth event as it unfolds and just "go with the flow." An expectant mother's illness may affect the delivery she had planned; the original plan may have to change somewhat, but your being there doesn't have to change, and shouldn't.

If a C-section becomes necessary you may not be allowed in the delivery room; sometimes even the husband isn't allowed. If you feel strongly about being present, you can ask; they may make an exception. If not, you can ask to be allowed to see your daughter or daughter-in-law as soon after the birth as possible. I was able to see my daughter in the recovery room immediately after her C-Section delivery of my grandson Erik. If your daughter has been heavily sedated she will be groggy and not remember much of the birth or her first moments with her baby. You can take pictures and tell her how everything went when she is more alert.

This is not the time to get into detailed discussions about how worried you were, how hard a time you had getting to the hospital, etc. More than anything else, she will want you to tell her how beautiful and healthy the baby is since this is always a mother's first concern. If the baby needs to go to the nursery for any required monitoring or problems, you will most likely be allowed to go into the nursery to visit your grandchild, and you should go. However, try to always keep your daughter and her well-being the primary focus, not the baby. The baby will get plenty of attention from everyone else. Don't let your daughter feel that all you care about is the heir. Sometimes grandparents in their excitement to see the new grandchild rush off to the nursery without even embracing their child, the new mother, first. Think of this as her "curtain call" and allow her all the accolades she so rightly deserves.

While not a calamity, the first week in July can be somewhat disorganized at the hospital because that is the week the first year residents or interns report for work fresh from their medical school graduations. They will be trying to orient themselves to the hospital and to become familiar with the staff and policies during this week. If your daughter has a choice, as in the case of a scheduled induction, she might want to avoid this week. If there is no choice, it is best to be aware that many of the residents may feel overly stimulated with excitement, exuberance, excessive expectations and perhaps even fear. If you understand this you may be able to communicate better with them to make the decisions that are necessary. It is reported that the busiest months for deliveries are July, August and September.

> "My daughter was so exhausted and drugged after the C-Section birth that she was not alert, so I got to take the baby and rock him for nearly an hour. I stroked his head and told him who I

was and why I was holding him instead of his
mother . . . that I was standing in for her." Pat,
grandmother

If your son-in-law is ill when your daughter goes into labor
you may have to be more of the coach than you had planned. If
he is contagious they may not even allow him in the room. While
it doesn't happen often, sometimes a new Dad is sick or
hospitalized or stuck at an airport or in traffic. So consider
yourself an under-study in this production. The nurse will help
you as labor unfolds. Nurses are trained in labor management
techniques and can guide you if you become the coach at the last
minute.

If for some reason your daughter goes into labor away from
home or for some other reason can't make it to the hospital, then
you may miss the birth. Just be grateful it went quickly and
safely for her and get to her as soon as you can. Just as with the
inevitable last minute calamities at weddings, these unexpected,
often exciting happenings at birth will probably be remembered
more than the rest of the birth experience and become the
favored part of the birth story.

"My second child was born at the home of his
grandmother, who had been disapproving of
home birth. When circumstances created a need
for us to use her home (our gas line broke,
meaning no hot water at our house) my mother-
in-law generously allowed us into her home.
Since she had delivered all three of her children
in the 50's under heavy sedation, she had never
actually been at a birth. The result was
wonderful. Besides having a healthy child, I
also was blessed with a much better relationship
with my mother-in-law." Nadia, mother

If your daughter's water breaks prematurely, which happens
in about fifteen percent of births or one in eight pregnancies,

then her hospital confinement plans may indeed change. However, it should not prevent you from being there. Her doctor will advise her to come to the hospital sooner than planned; because of the risk of infection and procedures may be implemented which otherwise would not have been considered. These procedures will most likely include internal fetal monitoring and an IV, but for the most part, your role should not be affected too much.

If the hospital is full and an LDR room is not available, the birth may take place in a combination of labor and delivery rooms. These rooms are smaller and the hospital may limit the number of people allowed in at any one time. Although you may not be able to stay in the room with your daughter throughout the delivery, you can wait in a nearby lounge and trade places occasionally with your son-in-law. This should still allow you to participate in measures to comfort your daughter and give you the opportunity to take some pictures. As soon as the birth is complete, you will be able to see her.

If there is an extreme emergency prior to birth and your daughter is rushed to surgery, her husband may not be allowed to stay with her. In that case, your comfort and companionship will be invaluable to him as he waits and vice versa. If everyone must wait in the waiting room, sharing your concern and prayers with other family members will help all of you.

> "My advice would be to tell everyone (who plans to attend the birth) what you think you want, but let them know that it might change. You may want everyone there, or you may ask everyone to leave. Don't make any promises in advance. Don't have anyone at your birth for their benefit, only yours." Sheila, mother

Many births do not go as planned--as dreamed.

Your daughter may be upset because she suffered a difficult birth. She may be angry and resentful. These feelings are normal after a hard birth and although she may not feel as close to the baby as she thought she would, this feeling will eventually subside as she comes to terms with her disappointment. It is not unusual for babies and moms to get off to a wrong start after a difficult birth. You can help by loving them both and not being judgmental.

Birth, while a memorable slice of life, is still an unwritten three-act play. About twenty percent of women with no apparent medical problem and no previous trouble with pregnancy develop some kind of problem during labor. All you know for sure is that it will unfold with surprises, drama, and a plethora of emotions. It may help to remind yourself that birth is an adventure, albeit an unknown one.

Chapter Twelve
Your Daughter Still Needs You

After the birth of a healthy infant, the family members usually go back to life as usual; that is, everyone except the new mother and father. Childbirth is not over yet. The fourth stage-- recovering--will take three to six months. The production is over, the curtain calls have been taken and now the actors must return to a normal life.

Some new moms suffer depression and a feeling of helplessness, no matter how much they wanted their baby or how rewarding the childbirth experience was. They are often scared, emotional, sick, and of course, tired.

As her mother, you still need to baby *your* baby so she can baby *her* baby better. While allowing your daughter and son-in-law some space to bond as a new family, you will still be needed more than you can imagine.

> "I remember feeling left out because my mother and my baby son were in all the pictures. I wasn't included because I was in bed much of the time, suffering from complications. I began to resent my mother, wondering whose baby it was--hers or mine? 'Look at me; I am hurting over here!' I remember thinking. I felt guilty because I was jealous of my own baby." Lynn, mother

Pictures of the new baby should include your daughter and son-in-law more than you. Pregnancy is a time when women are the center of attention for nine months. Not since their wedding day have they had so many people watching them and concerned about their every move. It is hard for a woman to go through birth and all of a sudden be pushed off center stage to become the wet-nurse, nanny, maid, and laundress to a wailing alien who is upstaging her.

Your daughter may also feel that she is no longer the cherished wife, but has been relegated to the position of the "baby's mother". She may feel she has been given a list of chores to accomplish for which she will be judged. Most new mothers need to be reassured that they are valued for themselves, and that they are a good mother to their new infant. No amount of encouragement in their ability is too much. Many women are scared of not being the kind of caregiver to their child that they always wanted to be. Diplomacy is very important for the first few weeks. Make all of her reviews positive and glorious; reassurance will help relieve most anxiety. As she cares for her infant in the months to come, a new mother begins to realize she possesses the ability to soothe her infant as no one else can. An infant will know his mother or father by their touch, their voice, and their smell and show a preference to them over other caregivers. Sometimes a distraught infant can be calmed by being placed near the mother's nightgown

> "I worried…that I would want to be alone with my husband and baby after the birth and I didn't want anyone to stay with us or visit too much. That was a laugh. After the birth I needed my mom with me more than ever and I loved having visitors (at least in the first week)." Sheila, mother

In the days following birth new mothers are extremely tired. The euphoria and energy which engulfed them immediately after they delivered is replaced with an overwhelming exhaustion. Their husbands may be very willing and able to help, but if they can't, due to work commitments, then getting outside help is a must. You can be a lot of help if you live in the area or if you stay in town for a few days. Rocking or bathing the baby so your daughter can get an extra hour of sleep, is a real gift. Taking the baby for a walk or to a park (which, by the way, is not just a summer day activity; women in Norway take their bundled babies out all year), may offer your daughter some time to privately talk to her best friend, or doze. Sleep means more to her than even food; and food, lots of food, is a big priority now. She will find it hard to get enough to eat but will not have the energy to shop and prepare wholesome meals. Preparing meals for the first few weeks is another great way for you to help everyone.

> "My plan is to take care of the cleaning, cooking, etc. I will be staying with her (my daughter) for a few days after the birth. I also don't want my daughter to feel left out - people coming to see the baby, not her." Denese, grandmother

Afterpains (uterine contractions after birth) occur with intensity in the days after delivery, particularly after a second baby, and are very uncomfortable during nursing because nipple stimulation releases oxytocin (as mentioned earlier)which causes the contractions. They will subside in a few days. A full bladder will make the afterpains worse, so you might suggest she empty her bladder before she nurses. If your daughter is suffering with these pains she should take an over-the-counter pain relief medication or consult her doctor. I mention this malady because some women are not prepared for these contractions occurring after delivery. They missed this piece of information in their childbirth classes or no one mentioned it.

Breastfeeding (nursing) will add an additional strain to your daughter's fatigue and anxiety. I have never known anyone who breezed through breastfeeding without any problems, especially the first time. If you breastfed your children, you may be able to eliminate some common problems before they become severe. You can also remind your daughter of organizations she can call for help such as La Leche League. She may not listen to you even if you do make suggestions as sometimes daughters balk when mothers try to help. She might be more open to suggestions from her pediatrician or the experts at the breastfeeding sources I have listed at the end of the book. (Her obstetrician is not the person to answer questions regarding breastfeeding. In most cases, OB/GYN residents don't have a formal course on breastfeeding. They are, therefore, not as knowledgeable as you might expect them to be.) Remember, she is experiencing many conflicting emotions. If she will not call, then you make the call for her and ask the individual at the organization to call her back. Breastfeeding requires a lot of rest, liquids, patience, quiet and support to be successful. Without help and knowledge, it can be painful, tiring, and may even bring on illness in the way of a breast infection. While it is a natural function for your body to produce milk after birth, it is a learned behavior to know how to nurse a baby. The teachers of nursing--midwives, mothers and friends who were part of the extended family in past generations aiding the mother and baby team, are no longer there.

Your feelings about breastfeeding may influence your daughter a lot, second only to her husband. If she is having problems, try to support her decision to breastfeed and not opt for the easy way out, formula, at the first sign of trouble. Even though that would allow you more time to hold the baby and her more time to sleep, the ultimate result if breastfeeding is abandoned could be a feeling of severe disappointment by your daughter that she was unable to give her baby what every professional agrees is best. Her sense of failure if she truly wanted to breastfeed will hurt her worse than losing some sleep.

Breastfeeding is worth the effort in a lot of ways. The American Academy of Pediatrics endorses breast milk as the most appropriate nutrient for babies and believes breast milk alone will provide all the nourishment required by an infant for up to six months. Breast milk offers many nutrients as well as immune protection against many diseases, allergies and infections. Given this, it is hard for me to believe that an educated parent would feed her infant anything else. In fact, breast milk is often a life-saving food for very sick infants. For this reason breast milk is often saved by mothers who have plenty and donated to breast banks. One is the Mothers' Milk Bank at Valley Medical Center in San Jose, California. Although the milk needs to be tested for HIV, hepatitis, TB, etc.

to ensure it is safe, breast milk from one mother is quite sufficient for another mother's infant and can be a wonderful gift.

Breastfeeding is better for the infant's mouth development. It promotes bonding by its inherent skin-to-skin contact. Breast milk is economical, always available at the right temperature, convenient and safe for any child to consume. Breastfeeding causes the uterus to contract quickly to its pre-pregnancy size and breastfeeding can be used as a natural method of spacing subsequent births. Breastfed babies do eat more often than bottle babies; because breast milk is such a perfect food, it is digested quicker and easier. For that reason, breastfed babies usually want to nurse every two to three hours during the first month. This is why new mothers need some help the first few weeks. Once breastfeeding is established the rewards become more evident, as the discomforts fade. Breastfeeding reduces the amount of colic, spitting up, and stained clothing experienced with formula fed infants. Breastfed babies' stools are more frequent but do not smell. Other children and family members experience a unique view of love and trust when they view a nursing infant suckling at the breast, gazing into his mother's eyes while his little fist holds on tight to her clothing. The act of breastfeeding releases mothering hormones to further bond a nursing mother to her infant. She is so closely tuned to her infant that her milk will start flowing if she even thinks about her baby. This event has caused many embarrassing moments for many nursing mothers who--while temporarily away from their infants shopping or dining out--"let down" their milk at the sound of someone else's baby crying. Breast pads or soft handkerchiefs inserted in a nursing bra accommodate this instinctual response.

If a new mother decides not to breastfeed, she also needs to be supported in her decision as this is her personal choice for her baby and herself regardless of how you feel. Your lack of support will only cause a rift between the two of you over something that is not of lifetime importance. Many thousands of healthy, happy babies were bottle fed, including probably you.

Some hospitals have a postnatal support nurse who contacts patients shortly after their discharge to offer support and encouragement and to assist with any problems. This can be a great help. If one calls, encourage your daughter to speak to them. Many states also have visiting home nurses available; you have only to call and arrange a visit. A visiting nurse in Seattle noticed that my daughter was jaundiced and recommended I seek medical help for her immediately. It may have saved her life. I didn't realize she was severely jaundiced and at risk.

Often depression arrives just as other obstacles in the first few weeks of adjustment have passed. Approximately ten percent of new mothers experience some form of postpartum depression. This depression (or as they used to call it, "the baby blues"), normally results from the flood of hormones every woman experiences after birth and is usually not serious. However, it can occasionally be a real problem. Talking to your daughter and reminding her that her hormones are affecting her moods and causing her to cry and feel sad, irritable, and hostile will often help. Remind her that what she is feeling is normal and will go away with rest and a little time. If she does not respond, then be sure to alert her husband and perhaps even her doctor. Remain in close contact with your daughter after the birth. If you detect any signs of severe postpartum depression, with symptoms of confusion, loss of ability to express emotion or a sense of hopelessness, try to encourage her to get help using the resources at the back of the book. If she won't make the call, then you make it. Severe depression, while rare, can be life threatening, though it need not be. Depression is very treatable.

Women don't get much experience in taking care of babies today. Many were never "baby sitters" when they were teenagers. Hospitals sometimes offer classes new mothers can attend; baby care classes may also be available on the in-house hospital TV channel. Your daughter should have some reference books on child care for those moments of panic--such as in the middle of the night when the baby won't stop crying. While she may think she knows everything, it won't take her forty-eight hours to realize she doesn't. Many women will have already purchased a book on infant care; if your daughter has not, this would be a nice gift. In addition, she will watch how you handle the baby and talk to the baby. Sometimes that is one of the most important ways she will learn. Infant care is not instinctual; it must be learned. While many things have changed since she was *your* baby such as sleeping positions, when solid food is introduced, and diapers and pins, the nurturing elements of baby care such as cuddling, rocking, cooing and smiling to soothe an infant have not.

I remember when my husband and I went to baby care classes recommended by our doctor in 1967. We were taught how to hold a baby (the football hold was my favorite) and how to bathe a baby in addition to dressing, feeding, diapering, and safety. What ever happened to these classes from the Red Cross? If they were mandatory for first time moms maybe there would be fewer babies drowning or being scalded in bathtubs.

Many women and husbands, too, think a woman's body returns to normal immediately after birth--like in the movies. I took my pre-pregnancy clothes to the hospital the first time I gave birth to wear home. Boy was I surprised. No one told me I would have to wear maternity clothes for awhile, that I would still look pregnant. Husbands and family members may make unintentionally hurtful remarks about a big stomach, weight gain, or wearing of maternity clothes after delivery. You should encourage your daughter to eat well--and often--and not to worry about her figure for at least three months--six if she is breastfeeding. Breastfeeding mothers need 1800 calories a day minimum, an additional 500-1000 calories than normal. Her body needs nutrients as it repairs itself; rebuilding for future blessed events. Support her by reminding her this "look" is normal and temporary and is a part of motherhood. Then provide encouragement to her in the months that follow when she begins to exercise and resume a non-pregnant diet.

Sometimes, because of excessive surges of hormones, new mothers experience extreme hair loss and complexion problems. Dealing with an unrecognizable body, as well as bald spots and hormonal acne can be a lot for anyone's ego to handle. Help your daughter by suggesting she get her hair done and maybe purchase some new make-up, while you baby-sit. Always remind her this is temporary and she is, as always, loved.

Husbands should understand that their wife will not feel as intimate or loving toward them after the birth of a baby because of "mothering hormones" which cause new mothers to be totally absorbed with their baby and their baby's care. Some women don't feel particularly attractive due to their strange bodies and the fluids they are secreting and it may take them a few weeks to respond to sexual advances appropriately. Even then, a crying baby can kill the spirit of romance. Men need to realize that while things will never be quite the same again, since they became a family, the amount of love there is to give and to receive has actually expanded.

It will take her body a few weeks to heal internally, so sex is usually postponed until after the six week checkup. Stitches, which do not require removal, will gradually disappear on their own. They can be mildly or terribly uncomfortable depending on the number and location. Most women complain more about the inevitable hemorrhoids childbirth brings than the stitches. Apparently, hemorrhoids are not mentioned in child birth classes and so their appearance surprises many women. Warm baths and soft cushions for sitting as well as over the counter remedies help dramatically.

Amazingly, with all the body has gone through, it usually returns to normal internally in a matter of weeks. The only complication might be an infection which would be indicated by a fever, change in discharge or a vaginal odor. If an infection of the uterus or vagina is suspected an immediate visit to the doctor is necessary.

A breast infection could exhibit a fever of over 101 degrees F. with a noticeable red, tender place on the affected breast and a flu-like feeling in the new mother. Nursing does not have to be stopped, in fact, continuing to nurse and empty the breast frequently is usually recommended. A warm shower with a fine spray of water on the breasts will relive a full breast comfortably. A phone call to the doctor to prescribe an antibiotic, rest and the use of a heating pad should cure the infection quickly. If ignored, however, a breast infection can become serious so encourage your daughter to rest and keep the breast empty.

The hardest job you will have is not to criticize. Avoid telling your daughter what to do and how to do it. This advice also applies to your son-in-law. Make suggestions only or wait to be asked for your opinion. You are building a long term relationship with this new grandchild and you are naturally anxious to start. You don't want your relationship with your daughter or son-in-law to suffer while you are doing it.

Chapter Thirteen
Don't Forget Grandpa

In all the excitement and "woman" stuff which is going on, do not forget your husband, the grandfather. He may be with you and participate in the complete birth experience or he may choose to stay in the waiting room until after the birth. Regardless of what he chooses, you can include him after the birth as much as possible.

See that he is in pictures with the baby and that he gets a chance to hold the baby. Encourage him to go to the nursery with you or to visit the baby himself. He may feel embarrassed to ask, thinking he is in the way. You be the one to suggest ways he can bond with his new grandchild. Don't let his shaking his head keep you from handing him the baby. He will enjoy it, no matter how scared he is, as long as you don't leave him with the precious package for too long at first or make him change a diaper. (With the disappearance of diaper pins due to disposable diapers, more and more men feel safe in changing a baby's diaper.)

If he isn't at the hospital, call him as soon as you can after the birth, maybe from the room, so he can hear his new grandchild in the background. Arrange to meet him at the hospital and take him to the nursery or to your daughter's room and give him some time to talk to his "little girl." Give him a picture of himself with his grandchild to take to work. Include him, if you can, right away in any preparations which you, your daughter and son-in-law are making for the baby. Discuss with him the arrangements for taking the baby home and the planing of a family dinner and baptism. If his grandchild is named after him, be sure and comment on it, expressing your delight.

If the baby's biological grandfather is not at the birth or in town--perhaps you are divorced or he is estranged from the family--call him as soon as possible or encourage your daughter to call him. If there has been a problem with their relationship in the past, the birth of a grandchild could initiate a new interest in resolving past differences.

If the birth takes place at home or at a birthing center, the grandfather may have witnessed the entire birth. I know several fathers who told their daughters that they would just wait in the other room and ended up being present during the birth. They were often surprised at the depth of their feelings and were not embarrassed at all. This is not a sexual event; birth is a life experience and a miracle.

Many men feel out of place in what is sometimes considered a "female" event. You may easily overlook grandpa in all the excitement while you are busy with the new baby and helping your daughter. Try not to forget him.

You could suggest that it would be in order to change your wills to include your new grandchild. You might talk about sending savings bonds on each birthday. If you are the type of grandparents who will put a bumper sticker on their car, you could get one for him announcing his new status or bragging about his grandchild. Or you could take this opportunity to buy him a new wallet and include the new baby's picture.

In all of this, you need to carve out some attention and time for him, too. Besides including him in the events and encouraging him to get to know his new grandchild, you and he need to bathe in the new grandparent euphoria together; to see each other new again as your lives are forever changed. For the both of you, a new era has been initiated. You are re-invented. You two, together, have a new adventure ahead.

> "My husband was able to attend the first grandchild's birth and he gave the support to both the new mother and father that they needed." Pat, grandmother

Chapter Fourteen
What if There is No Baby to Bring Home?

"To every thing there is a season, and a time to every purpose under the heaven: a time to be born, and a time to die; a time to plant, and a time to pluck up that which is planted;.." Ecclesiastes 3:1-2

Despite the best medical care and the health of the parents, some babies don't survive. Others have serious problems which prevent them from going home. Pregnancy and birth are full of perils. Your grandchild's birth may not have the story-book ending you imagined. As much as we try, we do not control the universe, nor are we able to dictate events with certainty.

Approximately one in one hundred pregnancies end in stillbirth. Stillbirth occurs when the baby dies in the womb after the 20th week of pregnancy or during labor. For more than fifty percent of all stillbirths, no known cause exists. Once it has been determined that the fetus has died, the pregnant woman is usually given the opportunity to wait at home for spontaneous labor (which could take up to three weeks) or to come in to the hospital for induction. A C-Section is rarely a consideration because it is major surgery and thus, reserved for emergencies. Most stillbirths are vaginal births where the pregnant woman must go through the same labor and delivery process as if she were having a healthy child. It helps if a woman has time to adjust to this heartbreaking news and the series of events which will follow. It allows her time to prepare to let go of her beloved baby. She should not be rushed. Many women chose to go home and wait for labor to begin naturally; many decide to be induced immediately. Whatever her decision, those around her need to be supportive. The unborn child is not a danger to her health.

This child is a real person to her--and perhaps to you too-- not just fetal tissue as some would have you believe. Lack of a birth certificate,(most states issue only a "fetus born dead" certificate), doesn't make this child less alive to the parents and grandparents. The delivery should be as pain-free as possible, with ample drugs being administered, since over-medicating the baby is not a concern.

After the infant is delivered--and usually you will be allowed to go through the labor and delivery with your daughter as planned--the family will be invited to hold the infant, dress him or her, take pictures, snip a lock of hair, and help take the footprints. I encourage you and your daughter and son-in-law to do all these things and spend as much time with this precious infant as you can. It will be the only time you will ever have with this child.

Your daughter needs you more than ever now but you may feel as though your strength has vanished. While grieving for your daughter's pain, you grieve simultaneously for the death of your grandchild. You may blame yourself and feel guilty--after all, grandparents should die before their grandchildren. You must try to help your daughter, though, and control your own grief for now. However selfish it is, she needs her mother to love and comfort her. She also needs you to show her how to behave. You may be the only one who can help her feel comfortable embracing this child; holding him, kissing him and taking his picture, by doing it first yourself.

Prior to his delivery, I agonized over my ability to hold and bathe and kiss my own stillborn grandson. I knew I should help my daughter gather as many memories of Joseph as she could. I kept thinking; I couldn't do it; that I had never touched a dead person before. Then he was delivered and I instantly loved him so much, that helping to weigh him, dress him, and to take his footprints came naturally. I kissed him and didn't want to let him go. Reluctantly, I placed him in my daughter's arms. I am proud I was able to show my unconditional love for this child and help my daughter feel at ease handling him too. I then allowed her and her husband some time alone with him so they could get to know him and cry together, be a family, without my presence.

I called and encouraged any other family members who wished to say hello and good-bye to Joseph to come to the hospital room for a short visit. We took lots of photographs.

All of these activities help the normal grieving process. Contact your pastor, rabbi or other spiritual leaders for additional assistance. There are many support groups and I would encourage you and your husband to not only bring them to your daughter's attention but to go with her to a meeting, if you can. Support groups offer help through regular meetings, phone consultation and even internet on-line chats and bulletin boards. All of you should grieve openly and together for as long after the delivery as you need to.

Unfortunately, society doesn't seem to treat stillbirth the same way it treats the death of an infant, as in SIDS (Sudden Infant Death Syndrome), even though it is four to five times more common. Family members are reluctant to mention the baby by name and may not think a memorial service is necessary. With stillbirth, everyone wants to forget and move on. They don't want to talk about it and erroneously believe the grieving couple doesn't want to either. Talking about it is the best thing anyone can do however, to cope with grief. That is why there are many support groups established.

Friends and co-workers ignore bringing the subject up and if they do they say the wrong, trite things. Even your daughter's doctor may seem embarrassed and not want to talk about it. The husband often rushes back to work, leaving his wife home alone, lonely and hurt.

We have come a long way since the days when the baby was whisked away without the mother ever seeing it, "for her own good," but we still have a way to go in treating stillbirth like any other death in the family. Health care professionals now realize that the family needs to bond with the infant and be able to grieve openly while collecting as many memories as possible in the short time they have with the child. They will help the family collect mementos such as a lock of hair, pictures, hospital paraphernalia. The staff will leave and allow a quiet time for the family, alone with the child. Most hospitals also have on staff a person who will counsel the family on many of the decisions which need to be made and prepare them for the choices they have, such as whether to have an autopsy and where to send the body when they leave the hospital. Husbands are encouraged to give their wife something to hold, like a basket of flowers, as she is wheeled out of the hospital on discharge day. This thoughtful gesture fills her empty arms.

The infant should be named, if he has not already been named, and have a burial or memorial service. Your daughter will need you to listen to her as she plans a funeral and mourns with empty, hurting arms and breasts swollen with milk which is no longer needed. Her stitches and hemorrhoids may hurt almost as much as her heart because they are a constant reminder of her loss. All the comfort and support you were willing to give her or planned on giving the baby, is doubly important now. Most of all, allow your daughter and son-in-law to talk about their precious child. It helps also if you acknowledge this grandchild to your friends when they ask how many grandchildren you have, rather than let your daughter think you have forgotten one.

When anyone asks me how many grandchildren I have, I reply that I have five; Erik, Laura, Thomas, Andrew and Joseph who is in heaven. I also keep a sweet picture of my grandson, Joseph, taken immediately after his delivery, framed, on my desk, along with my other grandchildren so he won't be forgotten.

> "I attended and participated in the delivery of my stillborn granddaughter. I am still crying and broken hearted for the pain my daughter went through. At first she did not even want to get out of bed and every time we talked she ended up crying, but a loving, caring tender husband and of course, her great Mom, have helped her see that it was not her fault." Sue, grandmother

Stillbirth is perhaps one of the worst final acts for the drama of birth, possibly because it is sudden, unexplained and final. For this reason I have spent more time on it. However, other events can leave you with no baby to take home, at least initially.

Premature birth occurs without warning, but is sometimes the end result of serious illness or accident. Depending on the time of the birth, the complications and outcome for the baby vary. About eleven percent of newborns in the United States (425,000) are premature (a birth that occurs before 37 weeks) and the numbers are rising. Even babies born between 27 and 30 weeks of pregnancy usually survive although they often experience some long term problems. The recent McCaughey septuplets were born at 31 weeks and their health has been pretty good considering their early delivery.

If the baby is less than five pounds, he may be considered at risk and need to remain in the hospital. Usually an infant remains in the hospital until near his original due date. While it is difficult to leave the hospital without a baby, today's modern equipment offers the families much optimism. A premature birth can be very frightening for your daughter and her husband but your support will be very important to their well being.

I have listed support groups for complicated pregnancies which might result in a premature birth. Some hospitals also have a local neonatal support group for parents. I encourage you and your daughter to contact these organizations if you anticipate this type of birth, or if it occurs.

Other illness or complications may keep your daughter and son-in-law from bringing their infant home immediately. Many times an ultrasound or a prenatal test may have indicated that the child will have problems, so the family may have had time to prepare. Resources for some known defects such as Down's Syndrome, spina bifida, and clef palate are listed at the back of the book. I urge you to contact these organizations for help, education and support.

As many as forty percent of all newborns develop physiologic jaundice, which is caused by an immature liver. Occurring on the third or fourth day, it may require short-term care at the hospital before the baby is released. Sometimes home treatment is available. This type of jaundice is not serious or life threatening if treated. It seems to be on the rise, but perhaps that is because more women leave the hospital earlier before it is caught and treated. Some studies have also suggested that the increase in the use of epidurals may be a factor.

A more severe case of jaundice, called abnormal jaundice, is caused by some incompatibility between the mother's and baby's blood types. It usually develops within the first twenty-four hours after birth and may require more aggressive treatment and hospital confinement. With today's treatments, jaundice rarely causes any long term harm. Talk to the hospital staff with your daughter and be a support to her and her husband in any decisions they must make.

Your daughter may need more help in the first few weeks if she has had to leave her baby at the hospital, because she may be trying to express breast milk at home and take it to the hospital daily. She may spend an extensive amount of time visiting her baby in the hospital nursery or NICU (Neonatal Intensive Care Unit). A baby and a new mother are a couple. They have been together for nine months and they need each other. Separating them is inhumane. In their efforts to see that their wife gets rest, husbands, as well as other family members, often try to prevent a new mother from seeing the infant as much as she wants. Try to support her needs and not dissuade her visits. Hospitals will usually supply cots so mothers can spend the night with a hospitalized infant. They will also supply an electric breast pump for collecting milk which can be saved for the baby if he is unable to nurse. This will also enable breasts to continue producing milk until he can suckle.

The neonatal intensive care units at some hospitals practice "Kangaroo Care" which is a method of providing skin contact between the mother and her sick infant several times a day even if it means removing the infant from the incubator. The mother snuggles her infant up under her blouse and between her breasts in a vertical position. This closeness appears to promote healing allowing earlier release from the hospital. Your taking a turn might be permitted.

Everyone in the family should put their needs on hold, as just about the only thing this mother will be able to focus on will be her infant. When her baby is out of danger, she will be able to give the other family members the time she previously awarded them. She is not deliberately withholding herself from you, her husband or other children. She is trying to heal a part of her body which is hurt--her infant. Your help in cooking and caring for the other children may be needed more than anything else at this time.

A baby's illness may cause the labor and birth plan to be changed or modified. If it does, then you will have to adjust to any new arrangements your daughter makes. You may not be able to attend the actual birth afterall.

Don't let it appear that since the baby is not perfect, you don't have the same enthusiasm for the birth which you may have exhibited before. Your reluctance to visit or hold your grandchild may be hurtful. This is a family event and a family emergency or tragedy. You need to be available to help in any way that you can. Your love and concern for your own flesh and blood will usually override any fears you have. Trust yourself to be empowered to help in a caring, loving, compassionate way as you are needed.

Although unpleasant, these events occur and are a part of the adventure of childbirth, just as death is a part of life. I believe these incidences are a result of nature and are not "God's will." I believe God mourns with us when life is unfair. While He did not promise us a perfect life, He did promise to always be with us for support.

The world is not perfect and you are not perfect. Accept that your grandchild may not be perfect either.

Chapter Fifteen
At Grandma's House

While I have tried to limit the subjects and events in this book to the birth and the immediate time before and after the birth, I feel I would be remiss if I didn't include some of the basic safety information everyone needs to remember when an infant or young child comes to visit.

When the new baby comes to grandma and grandpa's house, he or she may be visiting a home in which a baby has not lived for some time. If it has been over twenty years since you had a baby in your house, here are some important things to review.

Hot, Heavy, High, Hanging, Honey or Harmful:

Hot is probably one of the first words a child may learn, but it takes a long time before a child can respond appropriately and recognize hot things in order to avoid them. Be especially careful to watch a child around a barbecue grill and fireplace; pot handles should be turned toward the back of the stove out of reach and bath water should be tepid. Now might be a good time to lower the thermostat on your hot water heater in case the hot water is accidentally turned on. A baby's skin is much younger and therefore more sensitive than yours.

Heavy objects, such as lamps, irons, etc., should be firmly seated so they won't topple over if bumped and placed out of the immediate reach of young hands.

High objects, if attractive to young children, will be reached somehow just because they are forbidden. Make sure ladders, stools or boxes are unavailable for a child to climb to reach a forbidden object. It is probably better to remove the forbidden object altogether until he is older.

High chairs need to have a wide base and should meet the JPMA (Juvenile Products Manufacturers Association) guidelines. Since you may wish to have a high chair at your home for visits, make sure you know how to properly set it up and use it. Obviously, a child should never be left unattended in a high chair. Some grandparents like the clip-on style since they use them only occasionally. If you have this type, be sure not to use it with a glass or pedestal table. A tablecloth under the arms of this type of high chair will interfere with the friction hold and so should not be used either.

Hanging objects like blind cords are choking hazards. Other hanging objects like lamp cords, plants and pictures are dangerous to a toddler if placed too low. Shorten them or secure them out of the way.

Honey should not be given to children under one year. Honey of any kind can cause the food-poisoning botulism.

Harmful items to be put out of reach are prescription drugs, gasoline, cleaning solutions, dishwasher soap, mouthwash, over-the-counter drugs, fingernail products, and most of the other items which are in your medicine cabinet or under your sinks, in the laundry room or the garage. Approximately 1.8 million poisonings are reported every year. Kids can open anything! They have nimble, small fingers and are constantly in a discovery mode; they have the time and the patience to pursue any desired object until they succeed. Never underestimate their resourcefulness. Now is the time to clean out the garage and cupboards and use locks or place items on higher shelves out of sight. You may decide to put child locks on certain cupboards and drawers both inside and in the garage. Many plants are harmful if eaten, so check on the ones you may have in your home and relocate the poisonous ones. Keep the number for the poison center handy and know the weight and age of your grandchild. The emergency personnel will ask.

Bird, Beast and Fish:

I have talked about cats and dogs in other areas but a reminder here is appropriate. Pets can cause disease. Young children especially should be kept away from **bird** droppings, litter boxes and barnyard animal wastes, and reptiles. Even Petting Zoos, while popular, can be a source of illness because the fur of the animals may be contaminated. It is wise to limit exposure and to wash hands thoroughly after each visit or contact.

The products used for an aquarium including **fish** food may be toxic. Other items pose choking hazards. Keep all aquarium products away from children. Do not leave half full buckets of water from cleaning the aquarium unattended.

Sunburn, Stings, Strings, Sand, Salmonella, Sharps, Stairs, Sockets, Seats, Shots, Shaking, Smoking:

Sunburn and its long term consequences are gaining more attention every day. Every child over the age of six months should wear sunscreen, a hat, and sunglasses whenever they are out of doors. Children under 6 months should always be covered by a hat, an umbrella or both. The midday sun is the most dangerous, so avoid the beach or pool during the hours of 10:00 a.m.- 2:00 p.m. Wear light colored clothing.

Stings are not just painful and itchy; they can be the cause of serious disease.

Mosquitoes are a health hazard due to the diseases they may carry such as yellow fever, malaria, encephalitis, and a variety of viruses. Recently three people died from encephalitis in New York from mosquito bites. Children should be protected by a non-toxic repellent and the use of light-colored clothing with long pants and sleeves.

Bee stings can cause a severe allergic reaction, so a child should be watched for signs of distress, such as breathing difficulty, swelling in the mouth, and nausea if they have been stung. Know first aid and seek medical treatment immediately if any of these symptoms develop.

Ticks can spread Lyme disease, Ehrlichiosis, Relapsing Fever and Rocky Mountain Spotted Fever. Avoid walking in long grass and dress with as much covering as possible. Typhus can be carried by ticks, lice and fleas. If you have a pet, it is imperative that you keep your pet clean. Fleas are an irritant to everyone. Be sure your pet does not have fleas and has not brought them into your home before the baby crawls on your carpet. Flea collars are toxic and since babies put everything in their mouth, give your pet oral flea medicine. Store it out of reach.

Strings on jackets and hooded sweatshirts are a major cause of choking in children--they can catch on playground equipment. Newer clothing has been manufactured to eliminate these cords. Be watchful of hand-me-downs or garage sale items which may have been manufactured before this choking hazard was known. If you find them, remove them. Hoods of sweatshirts and jackets now have elastic rather than drawstrings.

Sandboxes are my personal pet peeve. No matter how you cover them, they still are a breeding ground for organisms, especially Pinworms. Also Hookworms are ingested from infected soil, usually where pets have frequented. Children get sand in their eyes and mouth. What fun is that? I think playing in sand should be left to older children or to occasional visits to the beach.

Salmonella and E-coli are much talked about in the news these days; and for good reason. Food poisoning strikes up to 81 million people every year. Children are especially susceptible because of their small size and immature immune systems. Unfortunately, we now have to assume all of our meat, poultry, eggs and shellfish is contaminated and make sure we cook it completely. Throw out any food left at room temperature for more than two hours. Offer only pasteurized cider, milk and juices to children, and wash all fruits and vegetables thoroughly. All cooking utensils and kitchen counters should be disinfected regularly. Products with raw eggs, like homemade mayonnaise, salad dressings, cookie dough, cake batter and eggnog should never be given to a child. The days of grandchildren licking the bowl are gone.

Salmonella is spread by reptiles also. Although nearly all animals can carry salmonella in their feces, reptiles are of special concern because they regularly shed the bacteria. Pet turtles and iguanas leave invisible and long-living contamination on whatever they touch. Alfalfa sprouts have been found to be contaminated with Salmonella and may not be a good food for children since it is difficult to wash them completely.

In order to minimize the risk of botulism, baby formula and food should not be reheated and reused a second time. You would not want to be the cause of making your grandchild sick. Times have changed since you were a kid. We worried about polio then; now we have to worry about our food supply.

Sharp objects, such as knives and scissors should, of course, be out of reach for toddlers. If you do crafts, remember to put your tools away before your grandchildren visit. Sharp corners on furniture are a common cause of head injury to young children. If you have a glass-top table or an extremely pointed coffee table, maybe now is the time to get a new one made of solid wood with rounded corners.

Stairs are a leading cause of injury, especially with baby walkers(parents are encouraged to eliminate baby walkers from their infant furniture). Even a few stairs can be dangerous to a small child. Purchase a child gate and make sure you install it properly and consistently.

Electrical **sockets** should be covered when not in use. Some of the socket covers are now considered a choking hazard so check around to see what is approved. You can also move furniture to cover the sockets until the children get a little older.

Stools, and especially toilet **seats**, pose danger. Even a young child can manage to climb up on a stool or chair and cause it to topple over. Put them out of the way or push them under the table or counter routinely.

The toilet seat should be considered the same as a swimming pool to anyone under two. Babies fall in, and because their heads are the biggest part of their bodies they cannot lift themselves out. Flushing their toys down the toilet or slamming the lid on their fingers, while unpleasant, is not the major worry with toilets. Drowning is a very serious and real threat.

Shots for your pets need updating. Be aware that many pets will not react favorably to young children, so expose your grandchild gradually to your pet. Avoid a situation where your pet may be impelled to bite, such as allowing a crawling baby to interfere with your pet as he eats. Most of the 4.7 million people who are bitten by dogs each year are children. Ten percent of all emergency room visits are due to animal bites. Male neutered dogs of un-dominating breeds are the least likely to bite. When there are dogs in the neighborhood, make sure your grandchild is in a fenced yard and you are with him. As an added precaution consider having a chemical spray with you when taking your grandchild for a stroll to subdue any unattended pet who may attack.

Shaking an infant in any way can cause serious harm or even death. In the old days, fathers used to throw the baby in the air and catch it, but recent studies suggest a baby may suffer serious nervous system damage or death with even minimal jarring. NEVER SHAKE A BABY!

Second hand **smoke** is extremely harmful to babies. It has been linked to Sudden Infant Death Syndrome and is known to be a carcinogen. If you smoke, do not smoke around your grandchild or when infants or children are visiting. Keep matches and lighters out of sight and reach of young ones.

Corners, Cuts, Choking, Crib, Car Seats, Carts, Copper Pennies:

Corners of tables, when sharp, have already been addressed. Let's also address the corner of your block if you live in a neighborhood of homes. Unfortunately, we live in a society where children are stolen. Two hundred to three hundred children are abducted by strangers each year, often within several feet of the parent. (These are children not taken by a family member or parent in a custody dispute.) Most of these children are never seen alive again. No child should be left unattended, even catching the school bus at the corner. The former rule of letting a young child ride his bike to the corner and back may need to be re-evaluated.

Cuts should be avoidable in a childproof home with proper supervision. Knives and scissors are put away and sharp objects are out of reach; or are they? Is there a razor on the bathroom sink? Is there an open can or lid in the recycling bin? Are there nails sticking out from the edge of the couch legs? Is an edge of the lamp base sharp metal, or is the screen door frayed? If any of these items apply to your home, then you should remove or repair them.

Choking is a leading cause of death of young children. Certain foods, such as snack chips, peanuts and hard candy are hazardous. Hot dogs and apples in bite size pieces are also dangerous. Small toys meant for older children are often picked up by toddlers crawling on the floor. To be safe for a toddler, an object should not be able to pass through a cardboard toilet tube. Read the labels on toys before you buy them to make sure they are age-appropriate, and separate older and younger children's toys. Avoid balloons. When burst, the pieces present a major choking risk to small children. If you do not know how to treat a young child or infant who is choking contact your local Red Cross and attend an instructional class.

Crib rails should be no more than 2-3/8 inches apart to prevent a baby's head from sliding through. Some older cribs from garage sales may not meet this safety requirement. If you want to have a crib available for sleeping over, be sure it meets the JPMA standards with the appropriate sized bumper pads and sheets. Never use plastic bags or a pillow in an infant's bed. Rails on decorative porch fencing and stairs should also meet this requirement.

Car seats for children and infants should be age-appropriate and always placed in the back seat of the car. It is unsafe for children in any type of car seat to be in the front seat. They are better protected in the back seat. Remember the front passenger seat used to be called the "suicide seat" because it was the most dangerous place to sit in the car. With air bags this is no longer true, but air bags are designed for adults and can cause harm to smaller, younger individuals. They are deadly to infants in a rear facing car seat even if the seat is placed in the middle of the front seat between air bags. All rear facing infant car seats should be placed in the back seat. Parents have as yet not been able to get this message, even educated ones, and so car manufacturers are being forced to respond to this danger. I cannot repeat the message enough. Even if your car has no passenger air bag, an infant is still safer in the back seat. Most states require a child older than one year be confined with a seat belt and children younger than one year be restrained in a car seat. Car seats accommodate children up to 40 pounds and booster seats with lap belt will accommodate children up to 60 pounds after which a seat belt alone is safe. Read the manufacturers instructions and install all car seats properly. Use car seats or safety belts *every time* your grandchild is in the car no matter how short the ride. Car accidents, the number one cause of death in children under 15 years of age, kill over 2,000 youngsters every year in this country.

Grocery **Cart** child seats are a convenience for shoppers but a danger to children. More than 20,000 children a year are injured in accidents involving grocery carts. Manufacturers and retail outlets provide straps on carts but they are sometimes missing or not used. All young children need to be strapped in. In the moment it takes to read a label, a child can go over the side hitting the hard floor. There are supplemental retaining devises available to purchase in the infant sections of retail stores. If you call *Baby Comfort Straps* at 1-800-546-1996 they can direct you to a store nearby. In addition, don't leave a child sitting in a grocery cart in one aisle while you run to another aisle to pick up something you have forgotten. Your grandchild is too precious to take a chance that someone might snatch him or her.

Copper pennies are not made of copper. If they were minted after 1982 they are 97.5 percent zinc. They react with stomach acid and can cause ulcers and illness. Bowel obstruction is only one of the concerns. Playing with money, feeding piggy banks and teaching how to count money is best done only with older children. Keep all coins out of reach of babies and toddlers.

Viruses:

While you cannot protect your grandchild from ever getting sick, I thought you might like to be aware of some of the viruses lurking around you. Frequent hand washing is the only preventative measure you can implement that might help. You can also offer to baby-sit more so your grandchild doesn't have to go to daycare any more than necessary. Daycare children are exposed to about seventy-five percent more infectious agents than children who stay at home. Frequent washing of toys and hands is still a good health rule to prevent many contagious infections.

The Rotavirus is a bug that is easily passed from child to child and kills between twenty and forty children annually in the United States. It causes severe diarrhea and dehydration requiring the hospitalization of 55,000 infants and children each year. There is a new vaccine to protect children from this virus and it should be widely available by the time you read this book. It is recommended only for infants under the age of six. Use this as a reminder that prolonged diarrhea and vomiting can quickly cause severe dehydration in young children and infants posing a major health threat. If your grandchild gets sick at your house don't hesitate to seek help.

The Hanta Virus is found in the droppings of certain mice and can be very dangerous. Four in every ten people who contact the virus die from it. While it is seen mostly in the desert portions of the Southwest, any mice infestation is a general health risk. All cabins, summer homes, barns and nearby fields where mice are located should be off limits until the mice population and droppings are eliminated.

Water, Windows:

Water, anything more than a melted Popsicle on your kitchen floor, should be considered dangerous. An infant can drown in two to three inches of water: in a mop pail, toilet, bathtub, wading pool or aquarium. Drowning is the third most common cause of accidental death among children. If you have a pool, then you will need to take additional precautions, perhaps by installing a pool alarm in addition to the fence and locked gate which most states require. Never assume any floatation device is adequate protection. Constant supervision is required. This might be a good time to take CPR if you have not already done so. CPR for children is different than for adults. Find a class in your neighborhood.

While water parks are very popular the chlorine in most commercial pools is not enough to kill off Crytosporidium, a tiny parasite that can cause diarrhea. Other infectious diseases that can cause infection from pool water are salmonella, hepatitis A and E. coli. Pools become contaminated from feces from dirty diapers or children's accidents. In 1995 and 1996 nearly 10,000 people got sick because they swam in contaminated pools, lakes, or rivers according to the Center for Disease Control. Nearly all of the large outbreaks of disease from pool water have been blamed on babies. Try to encourage youngsters not to drink the water, blow bubbles or make water spouts, just in case. Instead use backyard pools as much as possible where contamination and chlorine can be checked and regulated closer. If a child defecates in the water, the pool should be evacuated. Swimmers should stay out of the water for an hour or more depending on the size of the pool. Do everyone a favor and don't take children to public pools unless they are potty trained. When you do use Huggies Little Swimmers or reusable swim diapers made by Water Safety Products (1-800-987-7238).

Windows must be secured if you live in a multi-level building. Children fall out of windows more than you might imagine. Open double-hung windows from the top only. Use window locks to safely lock sash windows at a safe opening level. Screens are made to install and remove easily, so they cannot be depended upon to stay in place against the pushing weight of a child. Install safety glass on sliding glass doors and decorate them with decals so the glass can be seen.

All children will have minor accidents and illnesses as they grow up, but we need to do all we can do to make childhood as safe as possible for our grandchildren. Some phone numbers which might be helpful such as the Consumer Product Safety Commission are listed at the back of the book.

Appendix A: Resources and Sources

Childbirth Preparation Books:

Poliakin, Raymond, I., M.D. *What You Didn't Think to Ask Your Obstetrician.* Chicago: Contemporary Books, 1994.

Rosegg-McCutcheon, Susan. *Natural Childbirth, the Bradley Way.* New York: Dutton, 1985.

Savage, Beverly, and Simkin, Diana. *Preparation for Birth: The Complete Guide to the Lamaze Method.* New York: Balloantine/Ramdom Huse, 1987.

Simkin, Penny; Whalley, Janet; and Keppler, Ann. *Pregnancy, Childbirth, and the Newborn: A Complete Guide for Expectant Parents.* Minnetonka, MN: Meadowbrook, 1991.

Sears, Dr. William & Martha. *The Birth Book.* New York: Little, Brown & Co, 1994.

Jones, Carl. *Childbirth Choices Today.* Secaucus, NJ: Citadell Press, 1995.

Eisenberg,Arlene. *What to Expect When You're Expecting.* New York: Workman Publishing, 1984.

Congdon, Thomas. *Having Babies: Nine Months Inside an Obstetrical Practice.* New York: Simon & Schuster, 1994.

Childbirth Preparation Classes and Information:

International Childbirth Education Association (ICEA)
P O Box 20048
Minneapolis, MN 55420

124

612-854-8660, Fax 612-854-8772
800-624-4934
http:/www.icea.org

American Academy of Husband-Coached Childbirth
(AAHCC-Bradley)
P. O. Box 5224
Sherman Oaks, CA 91413-5224
800-423-2397 (800-4-ABIRTH)
In Calif. (818-788-6662)
http://www.bradleybirth.com

ASPO-Lamaze (The American Society for
Psychoprophylaxis in Obstetrics)
1200 - 19th St. N. W., Suite 300
Washington, D. C. 20036-2401
800-368-4404 or 202-857-1128
http://www.lamaze-childbirth.com
email: ASPO@SBA.com

DONA
Doulas Of North America
1100-23rd Ave. E.
Seattle, WA 98112
206-324-5440 or 206-325-1419
1-800-4-Doula
http://www.dona.com
email: ask DONA@aol.com
·

Call the hospital where delivery will take place to see what
classes they offer.

High Risk Pregnancy or Complications, Fetal Anomaly:

Minnock, Molly, MSW; Delp, Kathleen, ACSW; Ciotti, Mary, MD. A *Time to Decide, A Time To Heal.* Sarasota, FL: Pineapple Press, 1992.

Profit, Margie. *Protecting Your Baby-to-Be.* New York: Addison-Wesley, 1995.

Sidelines National Support Network
(Supporting women and their families who are experiencing pregnancy.)
P O Box 1808
Laguna Beach, CA 92652
714-497-2265
719-488-0432 (CO)
email: Sidelines@earthlink.net
http://www.earthlink.net/~sidelines

ACCH (Association for the Care of Children's Health, formerly, Parent Care, Inc.)
7910 Woodmont Ave., Suite 300
Bethesda, MD. 20814
800-808-2224
301-654-6549
Fax 301-986-4553
Email: acch@clark.net
www.ACCH.org

Cleft Palate Foundation
1829 E. Franklin St., Suite 1022
Chapel Hill, NC 27514
800-242-5338 (1-800-24-cleft)
919-933-9044
Fax 919-933-9604
email: cleftline@aol.com
www:cleft.com

National Down Syndrome Society
666 Broadway
New York, N. Y. 10012-2317
800-221-4602
212-460-9330
http://www.ndss.org
email: info@ndss.org

Spina Bifida Association of America
4590 MacArthur Blvd. NW
Suite 250
Washington, D. C. 20007-4226
800—621-3141
202-944-3285
Email: Spinabifda@aol.com

Cesarean Birth:

International Cesarean Awareness Network (ICAN)
c/o April Kubochka
1304 Kingsdale Ave.,
Redondo Beach, CA 90278
310-542-6400
http://www.childbirth.org/section/ICAN.html
Email: icaninc@aol.com

Cesarean Support Education & Concern (C/SEC, Inc.)
22 Forest Road
Framingham, MA 01701
508-877-8266

Twin Birth:

Twin Services, Inc.
P.O. Box 10066
Berkeley, CA. 94709
510-524-0863
Fax 510-524-0894
http://www.parentsplace.com
email: Twinservices@juno.com

National Organization of Mothers of Twins Club
P.O. Box 23188
Albuquerque, NM 87192
505-275-0955

CLIMB (Center for Loss in Multiple Birth)
P.O. Box 1064
Palmer, ALASKA 99645
907-746-6123

Breastfeeding:

The Womanly Art of Breastfeeding. New York:
Plume(Dutton),1997.

LeLeche League International
1400 North Meacham Rd.
Schaumburg, IL. 60173-4840
800-LALECHE (525-3243)
847-519-7730
http://www.lalecheleague.org

Postpartum Support:

Postpartum Support International
927 N. Kellogg Avenue
Santa Barbara, CA 93111
805-967-7636 Fax 805-967-0608
email: Thonikman@compuserve.com
http://www.iup.edu/an/postpartum

Depression After Delivery, P. O. Box 1282, Morrisville, PA, 19067, Call 800-94404773.

Pregnancy Loss (Stillbirth, Miscarriage, Infant Death):

Vredevelt, Pam. *Empty Arms*. Portland, OR: Multnomah Press, 1984.

Panuthos, Claudia; Romeo, Catherine. *Ended Beginnings*. S.Hadley, Massachusetts: Bergin & Garvey Publishers, Inc., 1984.

Kohner, Nancy; Henley, Alix. *When a Baby Dies*. San Francisco: Pandora Books, 1991.

Borg, Susan; Lasker, Judith. *When Pregnancy Fails*. New York: Beacon Press, 1989.

Isle, Sherokee; Burns, Linda Hammer. *Miscarriage: A Shattered Dream*. Minnesota: Wintergreen Press, 1985.

Lothrop, Hannah. *Losing Your Baby in Pregnancy or the First Year*. Tucson: Fisher Books, 1997

The Compassionate Friends, Inc.
P.O. Box 3696
Oak Brook, IL 60522-3696
Phone 630-990-0010

Fax 630-990-0246
www.compassionatefriends.org

SHARE (Pregnancy & Infant Loss Support, Inc,.)
St. Joseph's Health Center
300 First Capitol Drive
St. Charles, MO 63301-2893
314-947-6164, 800-821-6819 (Fax 314-947-7486)
http://www.nationalshareoffice.com

A.M.E.N.D (Aiding a Mother Experiencing Neonatal Death)
4324 Berrywick Terrace
St. Louis, MO. 63128
314-487-7582

RTS Bereavement Services(formerly Resolve Through
Sharing)
La Crosse Lutheran Hospital
Gundersen Lutheran Medical Center
1910 South Avenue
La Crosse, WI 54601
608-791-4747
800-362-9567 Ext 4747

Pen-Parents, Inc.
P.O. Box8738
Reno, NV. 89507-8738
702-826-7332 Fax 702-829-0866
PenParents@aol.com

Grandparenting:

Westheimer, Ruth K., Kaplan, Steven. *Grandparenthood.*
New York: Routledge, 1998.

Kitzinger, Sheila. *Becoming A Grandmother.* New York:
Scribner, 1996.

Karnhaber, Arthur, M. D.; Woodward, Kenneth L. *Grandparents, Grandchildren.* New York: Anchor Press/Doubleday, 1981.

Kornhaber, Arthur, M. D. *Grandparent Power.* New York: Random House, 1994.

Foundation for Grandparenting
5 Casa del Oro Lane
Santa Fe, NM 87505
Email: gpfound@trail.com
http://www.grandparenting.org

AARP Grandparent Information Center
601 E. Street, N. W.
Washington, D. C. 20049
1-800-424-3410
202-434-2277
http://www.AARP.org.connect.html

Child Safety:

Lansky, Vicki. *Baby Proofing Basics.* Chestnut Hill, Massachusetts: Safety First, 1991.

Consumer Product Safety Commission (CPSC) 1-800-638-2772

CPR for Children, call the American Heart Association 1-800-242-8721 to find a class near you.

Miscellaneous Web Sites:

http://www.childbirth.org
http://www.babynamer.com
http://wwwpregnancy.miningco.com
http://www.parents.com
http://www.pregnancy.com

Appendix B : Phone Numbers You May Need

Neighbors - for help
Hospital
Schools - for other children/grandchildren
Pediatrician - for new baby
Minister/Church - yours and your daughter's
Florist - near home, hospital
Son-in-law, work, car, beeper, parents
Your husband, work, car, club, etc.
Your mother and father
Your siblings
Your Other Children

Appendix C : What to Pack In **Your** Bag

1. This book.
2. Pen or pencil.
3. Paper or tablet.
4. Camera/film/camcorder with extra battery.
5. Map of hospital/parking information/address and phone number of hospital.
6. Address book of family members.
7. Phone credit card.
8. Snacks (they don't feed you).
9. Magazine or book, deck of cards, knitting, etc.
10. Change for phone or vending machines.
11. Music,(tape player), if desired.
12. Pictures of other children, grandchildren, of your daughter as an infant.
13. Instant hot pack, cold pack, lip balm, gum, suckers.
14. Wash cloth, toothbrush, toothpaste, and small towel for your use in freshening up.
15. Reading glasses.
16. Wrist watch.
17. Aspirin or prescription drugs you require.
18. Sweater or wrap.
19. Gift for your daughter and for the new baby.
20. Tape recorder to record first birth cry.

Appendix D : Your Memories of the Birth

(Do not write in library book.)

Glossary

Afterbirth - see placenta.

Anesthesia - pain eradicating medications (which cause loss of mobility and sensation) such as general, caudal, epidural spinal, and local.

Analgesic - pain reducing medications such as tranquilizers and narcotics, which cause no loss of mobility or sensation.

Artificial Rupture of Membranes (ARM) or Amniotomy - intentional tearing of the amniotic sac by use of a plastic device similar to a crochet needle which releases the amniotic fluid. The cervix must be dilated. This procedure is usually done to promote faster delivery. Also called "breaking the bag of water".

Augmentation - speeding up of labor.

Birth Center - free standing maternity center.

Cervix - opening at the mouth of the uterus.

Crowning - When the top of the baby's head is visible.

Dilate - to open, as when the cervix opens. Measurement used is centimeters, from one to ten with ten being completely open.

Doula - a woman who gives information about childbirth and physical and emotional support during labor.

Effacement - the thinning of the cervix during labor measured in percentages from 0 - 100%. The cervix must be completely thinned, 100% effaced, before active labor.

Engagement - estimate of the descent of the baby in the birth canal, from -4 to +4, with +4 being when the baby's head becomes visible, or crowns(same as station).

Electronic Fetal Monitor (EFM) - a portable machine that records the fetal heart rate (FHR) and intensity of uterine contractions on a continuous sheet of graph paper. The EFM is usually required when Pitocin is used. An EFM uses internal and external listening devices. A microphone picks up the heartbeat and it can be heard in the room if desired or turned off. A digital lighted number also flashes the heartbeats-per-minute.

Epidural - a local anesthetic administered during active labor (at about 4-5cm dilation) through a catheter in the lower back which numbs the nerves leading to the lower half of the body.

Episiotomy - an incision made by the doctor to enlarge the vaginal opening for the birth of a large baby or when forceps are used.

External Fetal Monitor -consists of two straps which are placed around the mother's abdomen and are attached to the EFM. One detects the fetal heart rate and the other responds to the pressure of the mother's contractions. The information is relayed to the EFM. See also internal fetal monitor.

Forceps - Metal instruments inserted vaginally which cradle the baby's head assisting the patient and doctor in the extraction of the infant from the pelvic outlet if a speedier delivery is required or if the baby's head is "stuck" after crowning or requires turning.

Internal Fetal Monitor - a wire with an electrode inserted into the vagina and cervix which is attached to the unborn baby's scalp to monitor and record the fetal heart rate on the EFM. Sometimes a pressure sensitive catheter is also inserted through the cervix and into the uterus to determine the intensity of the contractions. Internal monitoring requires that the cervix be dilated and the membranes (bag of water)broken. Internal monitoring is usually done when the external monitor readings look abnormal, when there is meconium(fetal bowel movement) in the amniotic fluid or when pitocin or an epidural is required.

LDR Room - (Labor Delivery Recovery) hospital room(suite) which replaces individual labor, delivery and recovery rooms with one room.

Meconium - baby's first intestinal discharge or bowel movement that may occur before, during or after birth. If it occurs before birth it may be a sign of distress but usually more indicators are needed to confirm distress such as closer monitoring.

Miscarriage - spontaneous loss of a fetus before the 20th week.

Neonatal - relating to the newborn or a newborn child.

NICU - Neonatal Intensive Care Unit - a unit in the hospital where fragile or sick infants are kept for closer observation and assistance.

Oxytocin - natural form of pitocin manufactured by the body as a hormone which produces contractions.

Perinatal - Around the time of birth.

Pitocin (Pit) - labor stimulating drug (synthetic oxytocin) administered intravenously through an automatic infusion pump at a prescribed rate causing or advancing uterine contractions. Administration of pitocin requires continual fetal monitoring.

Placenta - an organ inside the uterus which is attached to the baby by the umbilical cord and is essential for the development of the fetus. Also called the afterbirth.

Premature Birth, also Pre-term delivery - one which occurs before the 37th week of pregnancy or where the infant weighs 5-1/2 lbs. or less.

Station - how far the baby's head is in the pelvis; same as engagement.

Stillbirth - fetal death in utero (before birth) after twenty weeks gestation, when the fetus usually weighs over 17-1/2 ounces.

Triage - ongoing process of evaluating multiple patients to ensure that urgent care is provided to those who need it first.

Ultrasound - using sound waves, which bounce off internal structures, allows visualization of the fetus.

Vacuum extraction - a cap-like device which is applied to the fetal head assisting in the final delivery of the baby. It is connected to a rubber tube which produces suction. During contractions the physician gently pulls on the cap to assist the baby's descent. The suction will allow the doctor to hold the fetal head in place so it does not rise back up after each contraction; often used instead of forceps depending on doctor preference.

Topics

Where to find discussions of these subjects:

About the Author

Photo by Jeffrey Alan's Photography

Carolynn Bauer Zorn left her career as a sales engineer to pursue writing full time. She has a degree in Sociology from the University of Detroit/Mercy.

Carolynn grew up in Phoenix, Arizona where she attended Phoenix College. She lived in Chicago and Seattle before settling in the Detroit area where she raised her four children. She is also the grandmother of five.

She now resides in the Los Angeles area with her husband, Dave, who is a news broadcaster.

Her grandmother, Florence Marvyne Bauer, was a prolific biblical novelist and her grandfather, Dr. William Waldo Bauer, was a popular writer of health and family books. Her sister, Jamie Lyn Bauer, who also resides in the Los Angeles area, is a well known soap opera actress.

Carolynn is a member of the Ventura County Writers Club and the Society of Children's Book Writers and Illustrators.

Carolynn is currently working on a book about her grandson's tragic stillbirth.